CLASSICAL

SHOWTUNES

CLASSIC HITS

A Love Before Time
From 'Crouching Tiger, Hidden Dragon'

Music by Tan Dun

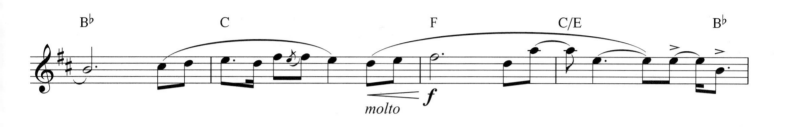

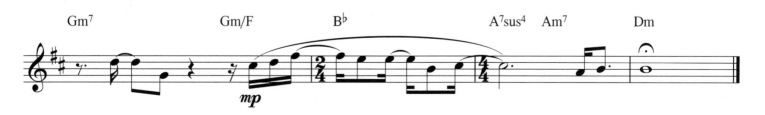

All Love Can Be

From 'A Beautiful Mind'

Words by Will Jennings
Music by James Horner

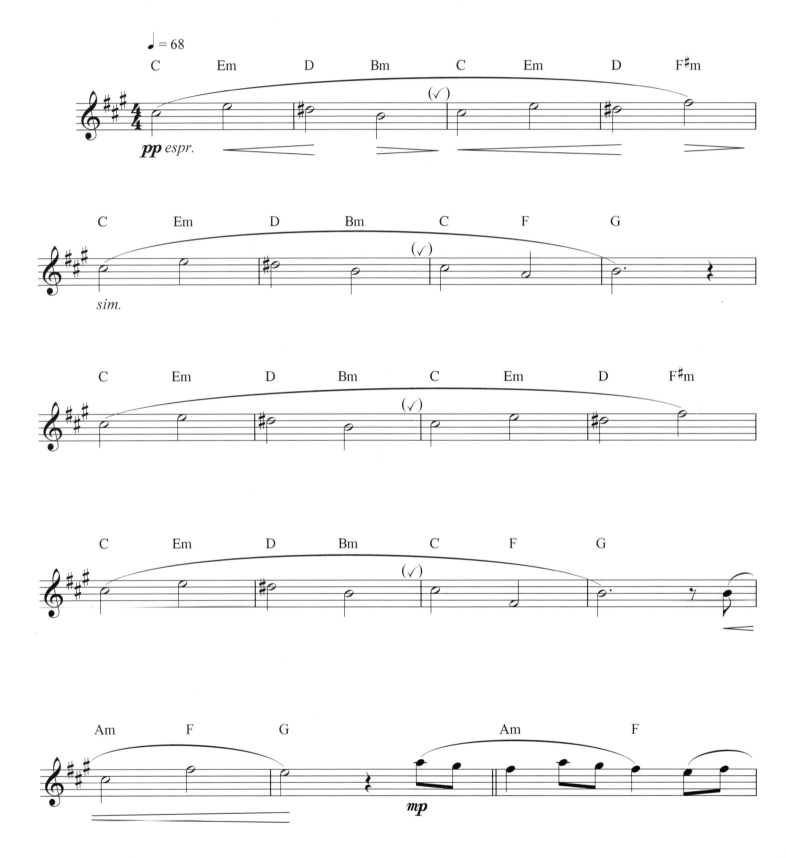

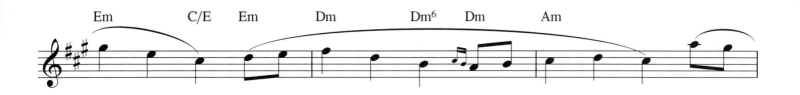

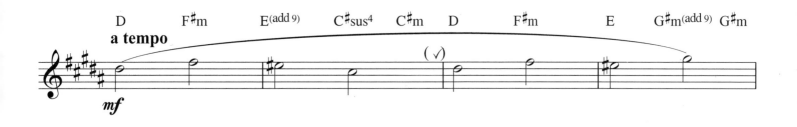

7

A Whole New World

From 'Aladdin'

Music by Alan Menken
Words by Tim Rice

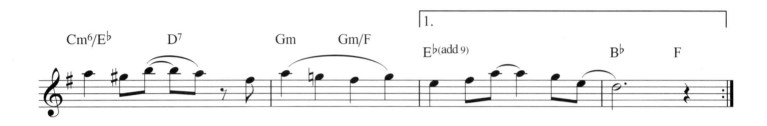

The Godfather
(Love Theme)

Music by Nino Rota

Goldfinger
(Theme)

Words by Leslie Bricusse & Anthony Newley
Music by John Barry

10

I Will Always Love You

From 'The Bodyguard'

Words & Music by Dolly Parton

Mission: Impossible
(Theme)

Music by Lalo Schifrin

My Heart Will Go On

Love Theme from 'Titanic'

Words by Will Jennings
Music by James Horner

Passage Of Time
From the Miramax Motion Picture 'Chocolat'

Music by Rachel Portman

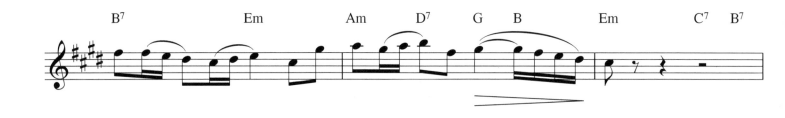

Moon River
From 'Breakfast At Tiffany's'

Words by Johnny Mercer
Music by Henry Mancini

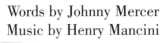

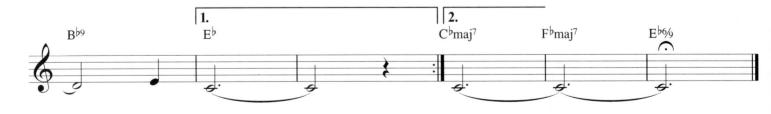

Don't Know Why

Words & Music by Jesse Harris

Angels

Words & Music by Robbie Williams & Guy Chambers

Beautiful

Words & Music by Linda Perry

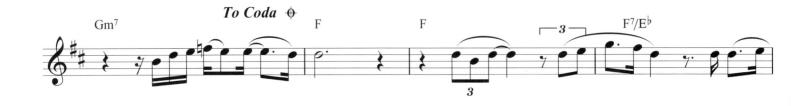

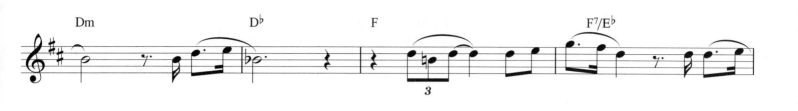

⊕ *Coda*

23

Crazy

Words & Music by Thomas Callaway, Brian Burton,
Gianfranco Reverberi & Gian Piero Reverberi

Don't Look Back In Anger

Words & Music by Noel Gallagher

Fields Of Gold

Words & Music by Sting

Put Your Records On

Words & Music by John Beck,
Steven Chrisanthou & Corinne Bailey Rae

Fix You

Words & Music by Coldplay, Guy Berryman,
Chris Martin, Jon Buckland & Will Champion

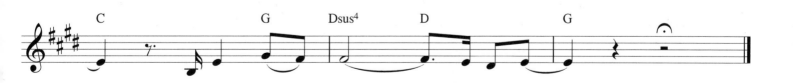

31

Nothing In My Way

Words & Music by Richard Hughes, James Sanger,
Tim Rice-Oxley & Tom Chaplin

Other Side Of The World

Words & Music by KT Tunstall & Martin Terefe

Ain't That A Kick In The Head

Words by Sammy Cahn
Music by Jimmy Van Heusen

Fly Me To The Moon (In Other Words)

Words & Music by Bart Howard

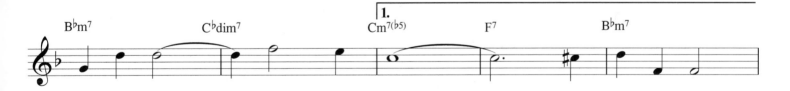

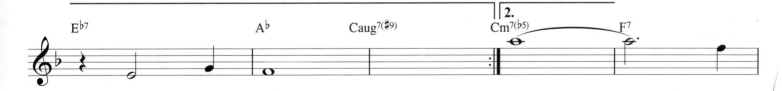

Besame Mucho

Words & Music by Consuelo Velazquez

38

Don't Get Around Much Anymore

Words by Bob Russell
Music by Duke Ellington

Fever

Words & Music by John Davenport & Eddie Cooley

Moderate jump beat

The Girl From Ipanema
(Garota De Ipanema)

Words by Vinicius De Moraes
Music by Antonio Carlos Jobim

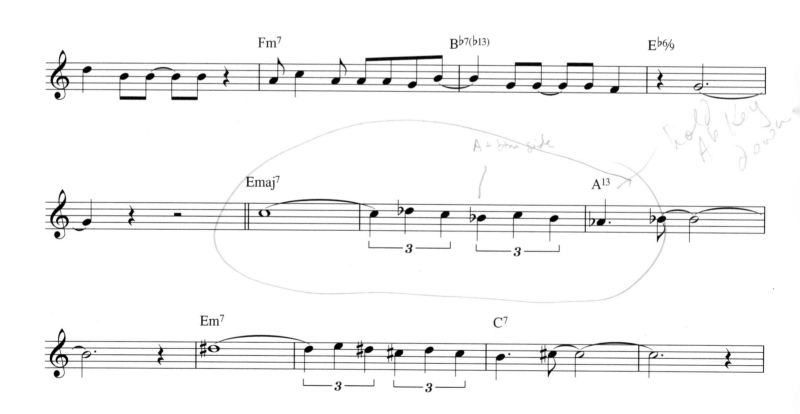

Moonglow

Words & Music by Will Hudson, Eddie De Lange & Irving Mills

46

Perdido

Words by Ervin Drake & Harry Lenk
Music by Juan Tizol

In A Sentimental Mood

Words & Music by Duke Ellington, Irving Mills & Manny Kurtz

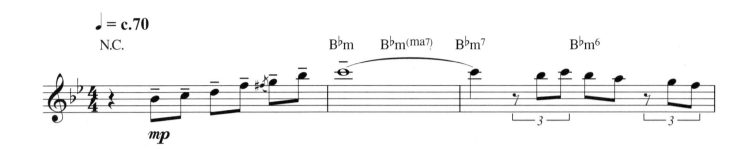

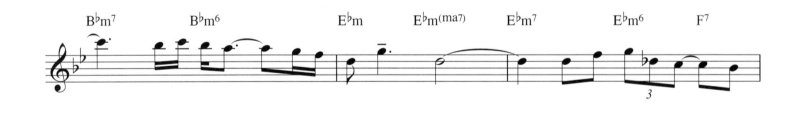

Satin Doll

Words by Johnny Mercer
Music by Duke Ellington & Billy Strayhorn

Barcarolle
From 'The Tales Of Hoffmann'

Music by Jacques Offenbach

Ave Maria

Music by Franz Schubert

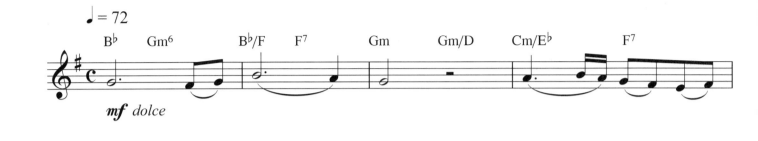

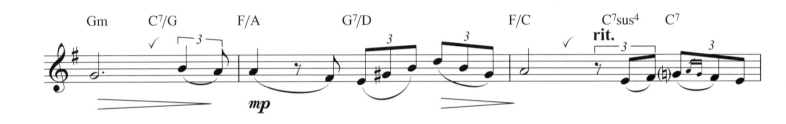

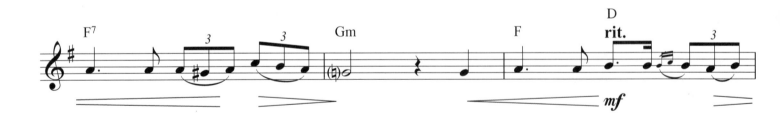

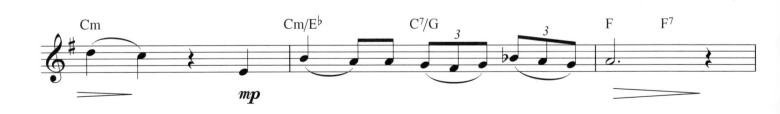

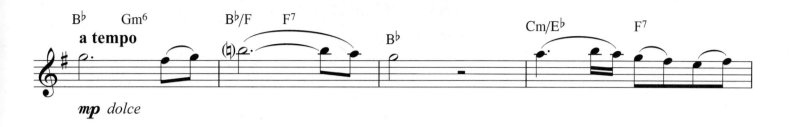
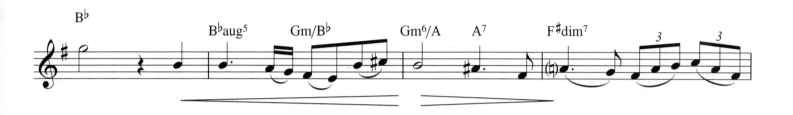
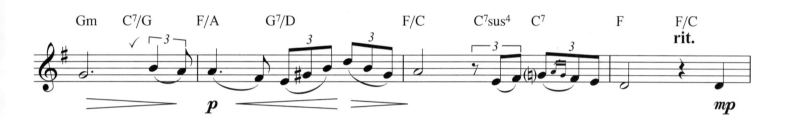
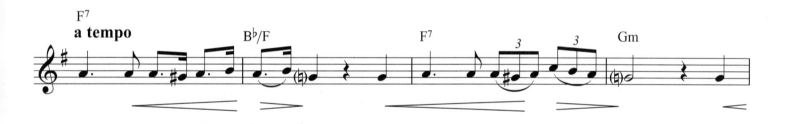
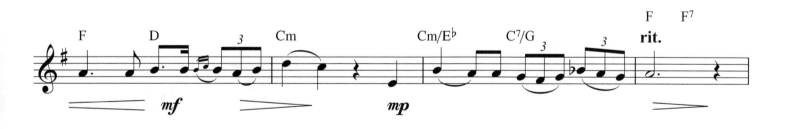
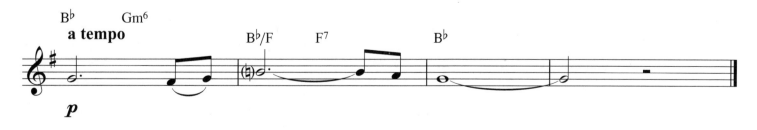

Clair de Lune

Music by Claude Debussy

Entr'acte
From 'Rosamunde'

Music by Franz Schubert

Gymnopédie No.1

Music by Erik Satie

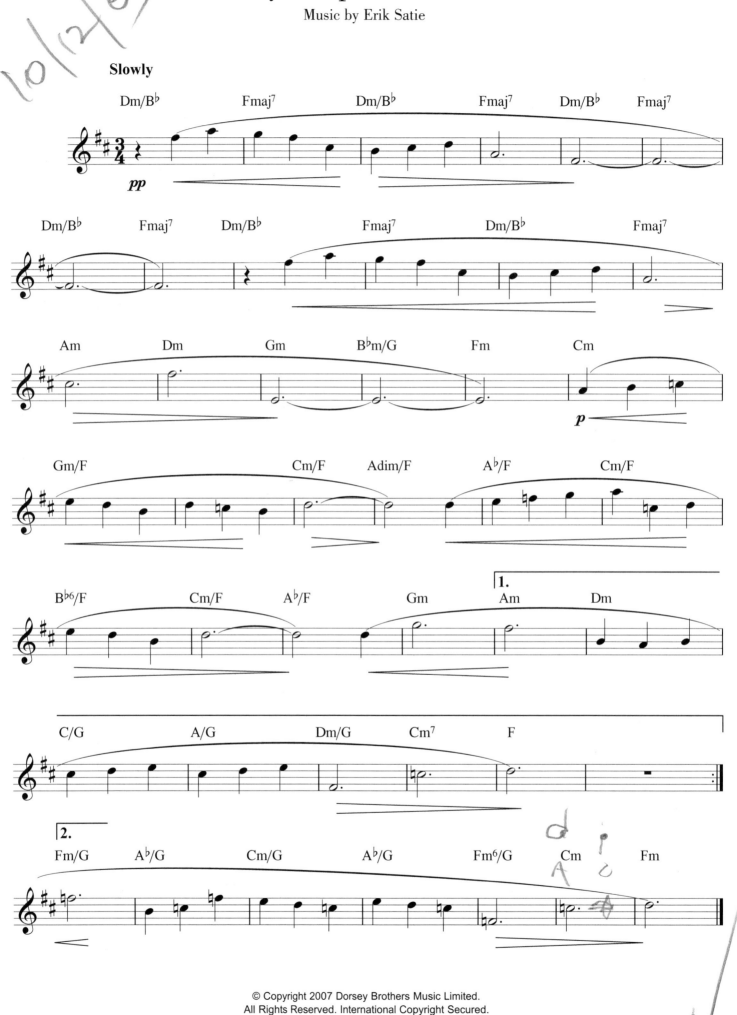

Largo
From 'Xerxes'

Music by George Frideric Handel

Jesu, Joy Of Man's Desiring

Music by Johann Sebastian Bach

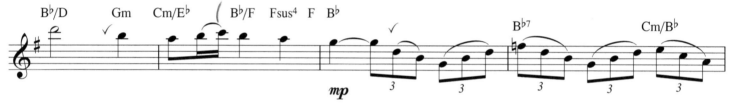

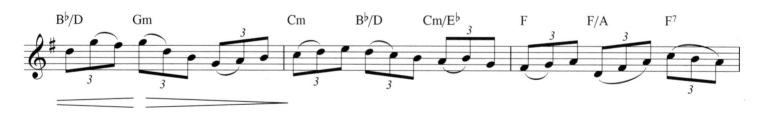

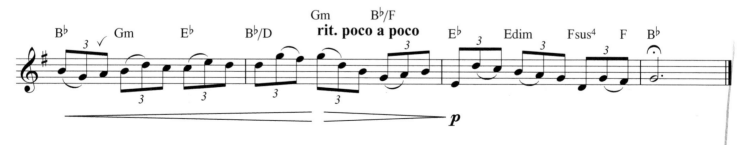

O For The Wings Of A Dove

Music by Felix Mendelssohn

Polovtsian Dance No.17
From 'Prince Igor'

Music by Alexander Borodin

Promenade
From 'Pictures At An Exhibition'

Music by Modest Mussorgsky

Any Dream Will Do

From 'Joseph And The Amazing Technicolor® Dreamcoat'

Music by Andrew Lloyd Webber
Lyrics by Tim Rice

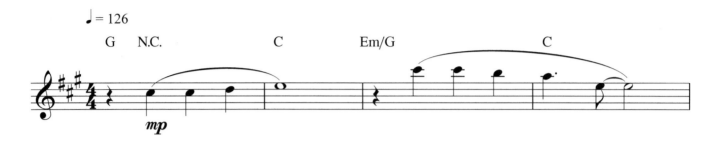

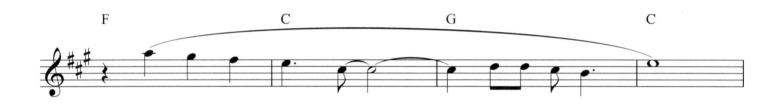

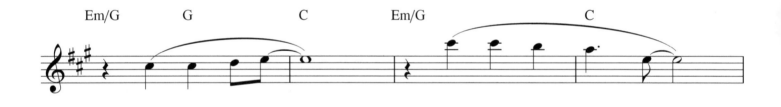

Can You Feel The Love Tonight

From 'The Lion King'

Words by Tim Rice
Music by Elton John

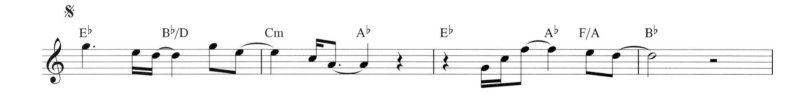

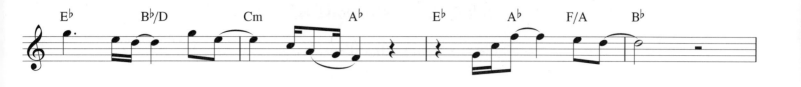

To Coda ⊕

D.S. al Coda

⊕ *Coda*

I Dreamed A Dream

From 'Les Misérables'

Music by Claude-Michel Schönberg
Original Lyrics by Alain Boublil & Jean-Marc Natel
English Lyrics by Herbert Kretzmer

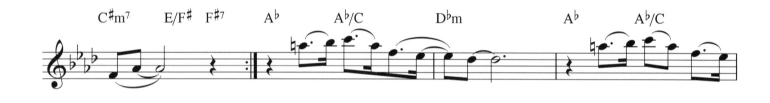

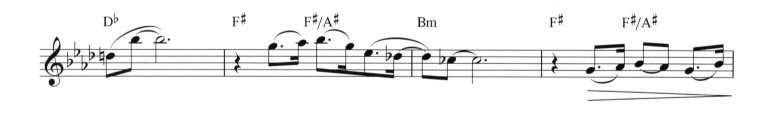

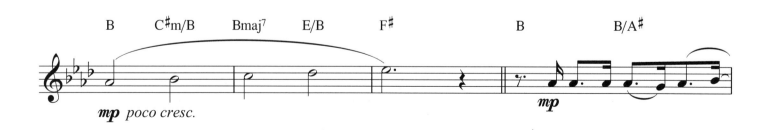

If I Were A Rich Man

From 'Fiddler On The Roof'

Words by Sheldon Harnick
Music by Jerry Bock

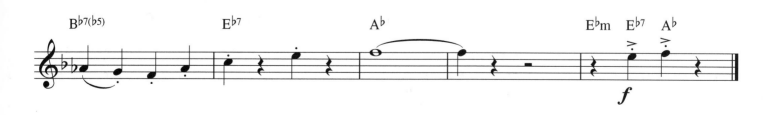

Don't Cry For Me Argentina

From 'Evita'

Music by Andrew Lloyd Webber
Lyrics by Tim Rice

Mamma Mia

From 'Mamma Mia'

Words & Music by Benny Andersson, Stig Anderson & Björn Ulvaeus

Memory
From 'Cats'

Music by Andrew Lloyd Webber
Text by Trevor Nunn after T.S. Eliot

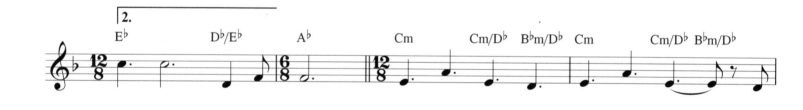

The Music Of The Night
From 'The Phantom Of The Opera'

Music by Andrew Lloyd Webber
Lyrics by Charles Hart

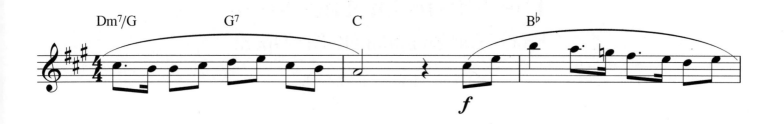

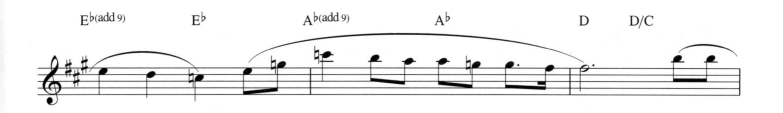

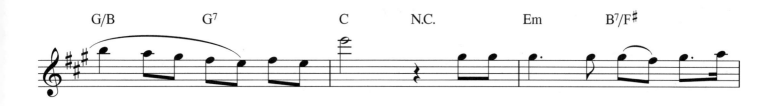

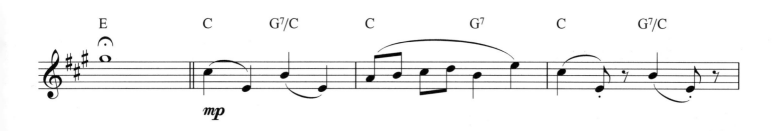

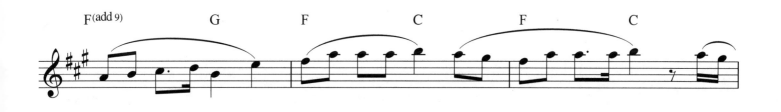

Willkommen

From 'Cabaret'

Words by Fred Ebb
Music by John Kander

You're The One That I Want
From 'Grease'

Words & Music by John Farrar

Angie

Words & Music by Mick Jagger & Keith Richards

Bridge Over Troubled Water

Words & Music by Paul Simon

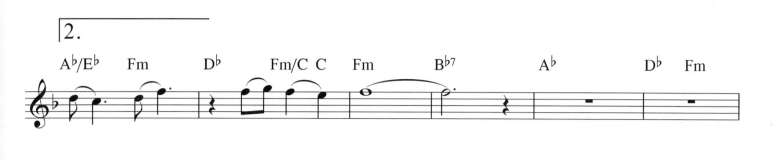

D.S. al ⊕ CODA

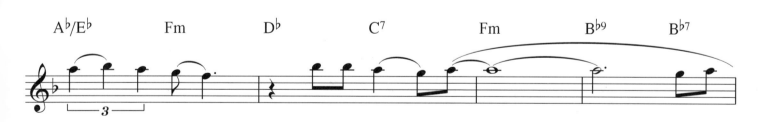

Can't Help Falling In Love

Words & Music by George David Weiss, Hugo Peretti & Luigi Creatore

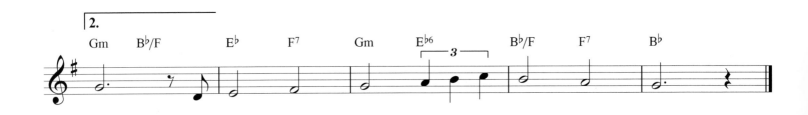

(Sittin' On) The Dock Of The Bay

Words & Music by Steve Cropper & Otis Redding

I Got You (I Feel Good)

Words & Music by James Brown

The Lady In Red

Words & Music by Chris De Burgh

Unchained Melody

Words by Hy Zaret
Music by Alex North

91

What A Wonderful World

Words & Music by George Weiss & Bob Thiele

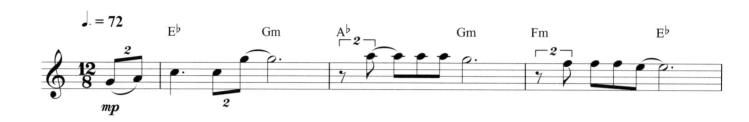

Stand By Me

Words & Music by Ben E. King, Jerry Leiber & Mike Stoller

Yesterday

Words & Music by John Lennon & Paul McCartney

Medium ballad ♩ = 98

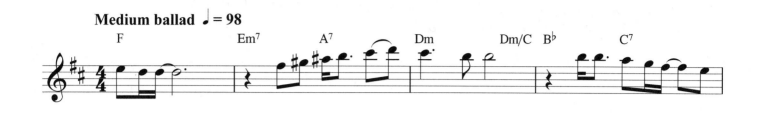

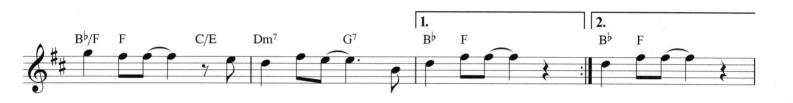

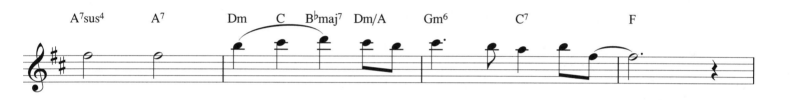

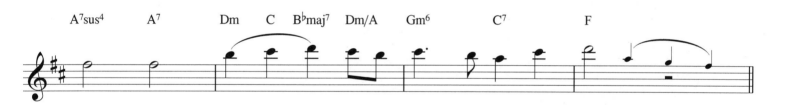

1 2 3 4 5 6 7 8 9

'Hand me my purse will you darling. A girl can't read that sort of thing without her lipstick.'

Audrey Hepburn
Breakfast at Tiffany's, 1961

Retro Makeup

Techniques for Applying the Vintage Look

Lauren Rennells

HRST
BOOKS

Cover Design, Illustrations, and Design by Benjamin Rennells
Photography and Design by Lauren Rennells unless otherwise noted

Published by HRST Books
Post Office Box 18429
Denver, Colorado 80218-8429 U.S.A.
info@hrstbooks.com; www.hrstbooks.com

Library of Congress Cataloging-in-Publication Data
Rennells, Lauren.
  Retro Makeup: Techniques for Applying the Vintage Look / by Lauren Rennells
        p. cm.
Includes bibliography.
ISBN-13: 978-0-9816639-2-0
1. Beauty, Personal. 2. Cosmetics. I. Title.

Library of Congress Control Number: 2011905239

Printed in the United States of America

Thank you

Many wonderful people helped make this book possible. First on the list are my parents for guiding me and standing with me on my journey, my brother Ben for being my design consultant and art director, and Rich for being patient with me. Thank you to my friends for being my cheerleaders through this process. A special thanks to my many teachers of beauty along my path including Miss Lil and Miss Cindy, Dena Olivett, Davida Simon, Leslie Snyder, Jenece Amella, Lorraine Altamura and the many other makeup artists I have had the honor of working along side of and have been inspired by. Thank you to Besame Cosmetics for helping provide historically accurate makeup colors in beautiful packaging that add so much to this book.

Thank you to all of the very beautiful models that sat for the book including Holly, Jordan, Keira, Alex, Amber, Kailee, Kira, Patricia, Destin, Pam, Devon, Erin, Kyleigh, Lorena, Jenece, Marianne, and the women of history in images scattered throughout the book. Your lovely faces make this book as beautiful as it can be.

Table of Contents

Notice to Readers

The reader is encouraged to take all safety precautions in performing any techniques or activities herein. By following the instructions the reader or anyone acting on behalf of the reader willingly assumes all risks of harm in connection with performing these techniques. The author and HRST Books are not liable or responsible to any person or entity with respect to any loss or damage caused, or alleged to have been caused, directly or indirectly, by the information contained in this book. Warning: Do not tweeze or wax eyebrows off completely. They may not grow back.

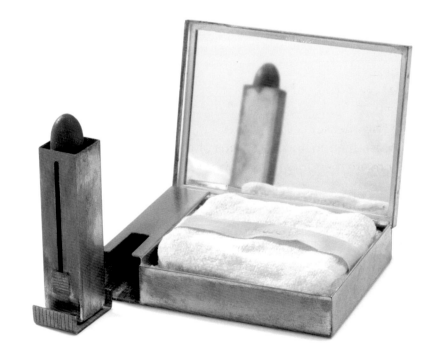

Introduction

Makeup is so common today that many of us do not give a second thought to its beginnings. Even though ancient Egyptians used kohl around their eyes and stains made from berries on their lips to enhance their appearance, the cosmetic industry as we know it today did not start to significantly develop until the 20th century. It is during this century that mass production and the media helped women all over the globe see the importance and beauty of *making up.*

This book provides a practical history and guide to application of makeup styles during these early years. There were great changes in the cosmetics industry beginning in the very early 1900s and continuing through the 1960s. Many of our ideas of classic beauty came about during these decades.

The research for this book unearthed so much more information than I had expected to find. The bits and pieces from books, magazines, and web sites have been combined to provide an overview of the looks of the different decades and detailed descriptions for more practical help.

When doing your own research for makeup looks you might like to emulate, check the local library, your parents' and grandparents' homes, web image searches, on-line auctions, and antique stores for books about Hollywood photographers, photographs, movies and other material. Watch movies and use your DVD player's pause button to pause the movie at different intervals and use your point-and-shoot digital camera with the flash turned off to capture makeup styles for reference later. Your computer's screencapture capabilities are also useful for this.

The Internet is absolutely the greatest resource. The Internet Movie Database, www.imdb.com, has information and numerous photographs of all the famous film actresses of the past, many of whom are mentioned in this book, and information on their movies.

No matter what your goal is in reading this book, I hope, above all else, that you will learn from it. Even if you are most interested in a specific decade, I encourage you to read the entire book completely. Understanding the beginnings of makeup application, and how it has changed over time can help you understand it as a whole, making your technique better.

A Little Her-story

"To sit before her dressing table at the end of a long full day in preparation for a long gay evening and be able to disregard those artificial means of youth, the rouge pot and the lip stick, is the privilege of only a few women, especially during the strenuous winter season...and the matron turns to the dressing table, her high altar, where she performs those mysterious ceremonies which double her natural beauty."
Vogue, 1915[1]

Victorian Era

Queen Victoria publicly declared makeup to be improper and vulgar during her reign in the late 19th century. Adding color to the face was not considered completely taboo by the average Victorian woman, but most often it was applied subtly so that no one was the wiser. Although these women were fine with using rubber bust enhancers and bustling their behinds, the false impression makeup provided was frowned upon.[2] Makeup was reserved for stage performers and prostitutes. There are some references that fashionable women carried "portable complexions" in their purses around 1870, but the majority of women's publications warned against it.[3]

Early cosmetic companies mostly sold creams and perfumes. These types of cosmetics were common on women's dressing tables in the 19th century. Although importers in the 1800s did bring in "Chinese boxes of color" containing red papers to wet for rouge, pearl powder, and eyebrow blackener, mass-produced makeup was not common in America until later.[4]

Home remedies to add color to the face for a natural looking enhancement were well known and written about. In an 1890 book titled *Homely Girl*, the author states, "A decoction of walnut hulls should be made in the right season and bottled. Applied to the brows and lashes with a fine hair pencil will turn them to a rich brown, which will harmonize well with fair hair."[5] Among other natural home beauty aids were crushed elderberries to stain lips and cheeks, lamp black to deepen lash and eyebrow color, or even pinching the cheeks or biting the lips to bring out a natural pink hue.

Edwardian Era

Attitudes toward makeup began to loosen up during the Edwardian Era of the very early 20th century. So much so did the acceptance of makeup take hold that in 1913 *Vogue* stated, "The little boxes of hard powder, each with its tiny puff, have become almost indispensable to womankind." For the first time powder cakes and rouge were packaged together in a box with a puff and mirror for touch-ups on the go.[6] King Edward VII's wife Queen Alexandra herself used cosmetics to improve her looks.[7]

The woman of the turn-of-the-century saw many innovations and therefore much more of her face. The process of mirror production was getting cheaper, and in 1900, George Eastman introduced the Brownie, a camera that anyone could afford. Before she knew it, the lady was seeing her image regularly and she wanted it to look better. She requested the paint at photographer's studios to enhance her portrait.[8]

The Theatre

Stage performers, even before the popularity of motion pictures, influenced the early acceptance of cosmetics for at least evening use. Theatre actresses such as Lillie Langtry were endorsing cosmetics and Russian ballet dancers with dramatic eye makeup performing in London increased sales of kohl and mascara.[9] Dancers can be credited with influencing many women who saw the beauty of a ballerina as something they might want to emulate. Both Elizabeth Arden and Helena Rubenstein attributed some of their attraction to makeup to seeing it on dancers on the stage.

The Suffragists

Women's suffrage was a hot issue in the early 1900s. In 1912, 500,000 people watched as 20,000 women marched the streets of New York City for the right to vote. They wore red lipstick as the defiant symbol of their right to make choices as women. Lipstick was still not a widely accepted makeup product, but it was making its way into the hands of many fashionable women.

Elizabeth Arden saw this mass of made-up faces and knew she was watching the beginning of a makeup movement. She joined the demonstrations, among many other high society women, and even used the rights of women as ad copy.[10]

Motion Pictures

By the late 1800s, motion pictures were gaining popularity. They had gone from being snippets of action played purely for art purposes to entire narratives telling stories of heroines and heros.

The actresses who played these heroines became the new role models and trendsetters for women who wanted to be fashionable. How they looked set the standard for what was beautiful.

Because these early films were silent, the pantomime of the actor's face was key to adding the tone and emotion of the individual scenes. The makeup was exaggerated to define the facial features as much as possible. With this heavily applied makeup and the newly developed close-up, the public was getting not only entertainment, but a lesson in how makeup should look.

Tools and Techniques

It is important to start with a good understanding of some basic tools and techniques that will aid in application and an attractive finished appearance. Read through this section carefully and study the basics before moving onto the full makeup looks in each decade chapter. There are some important things to consider on the following pages that will make the final look even more authentic.

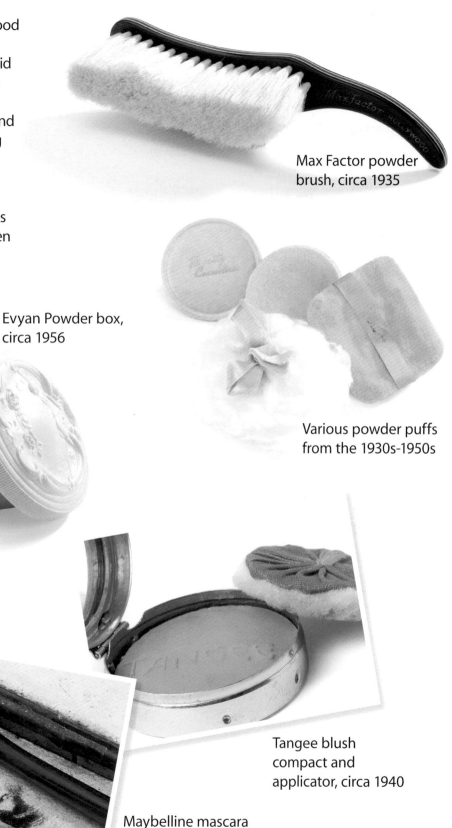

Max Factor powder brush, circa 1935

Evyan Powder box, circa 1956

Various powder puffs from the 1930s-1950s

Tangee blush compact and applicator, circa 1940

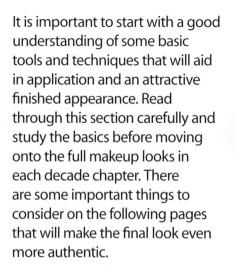

Maybelline mascara and brush, circa 1943

Tools of Today

There are hundreds of makeup brushes made by numerous companies today. This kind of selection was not available to women in the early 20th century, but luckily for us, they are available today, making application much more precise and controlled.

Be sure to clean your brushes on a regular basis to keep them sanitary.

1. Foundation Brush:
Foundation can be applied with a natural or synthetic hair brush or a sponge.

2. Concealer Brush:
Concealer brushes are usually small versions of foundation brushes with a finer tip for a more precise application.

3. Powder Brush:
Soft hairs allow for application of powder without disturbing the foundation and concealer underneath.

4. Blush Brush:
It is helpful to use a blush brush that is widely rounded on the end. The roundness distributes powder more softly for feathering

out. Flat brushes pop the color in one spot on contact.

5. Contour Brush:
Angled contour brushes are great for adding depth to the face by applying shading under the cheekbones.

6. Lip Brush:
Use a lip brush to apply lipstick more precisely after carefully drawing lip shape with lip liner.

7. Eye Shadow Brush:
A wide eye shadow brush evenly applies large amounts of color on the entire eyelid.

8. Angled Eye Shadow Brush:
By collecting eye shadow on the tip and applying directly, eye shadow color stays deep where the original application began and can then be blended out.

9. Smudging Brush:
Works well for blending or softening eyeliner.

10. Soft Liner Brush:
A small brush like this can produce fine powder lines with eye shadow.

11. Pointed Liner Brush:
When applying liquid or gel eyeliner, a fine, precise pointed brush is necessary.

12. Angled Liner Brush:
An angled liner brush is a good option for applying liquid or gel eyeliner. They are easy to control and drag color across the eyelid evenly.

13. Angled Eyebrow Brush:
This brush is similar to the angled eyeliner brush but not as thin. The blunt edge grabs eyebrow shadow easily for applying to eyebrows.

14. Eyebrow Wand:
An eyebrow wand looks like a clean mascara wand and brushes eyebrow hair more softly than traditional brow brushes. It also blends color that has been added to the eyebrows. Often eyebrow wand brushes and angled eyebrow brushes are on the same handle with a brush at either end.

15. Powder Puff:
A powder puff works best for setting foundations and liquids with powder.

Tip Throughout the book, the points of makeup pencils are referred to as sharp or dull and are used based on the best outcome for the desired effect. Some pencil sharpeners have a cap that rounds out the point of the pencil and other sharpeners cut to a sharp point. There are also convertible sharpeners that can do both.

Dull   *Sharp*

Contouring

Contouring is the use of light and dark to alter the visual appearance of a face. By adding lighter makeup to an area, it visually brings the area closer to the viewer. By adding darker makeup to an area, it visually recedes the area away from the viewer. Combinations of highlight and shadowing can be used to change the appearance of face shape.

Style of makeup helps determine an era but the basic shape of a face does also. Because certain types of face shapes were considered the ideal in popular culture during different decades, contouring the face to mimic those face shapes helps achieve a period look.

In the 1920s, small, sad eyes and thin lips were the look of many popular actresses. The 1930s woman might have a button nose or full lips. Beautifully contoured cheekbones replaced round apple cheeks in the 1940s. By the 1950s, high pointed eyebrows were the norm.

By studying the beauty of popular culture during a decade, a map of contouring can be designed. In the example below, Keira's strong, modern features are altered to mimic popular culture of the 1920s. Highlight added above the eyebrows and shadow added below flattens them. Highlight added slightly above the apples of the cheeks and shadow added at the bottom of the apples gives the appearance of lifting the apples of the cheeks higher. Covering the outer corners of her lips and adding highlight around them gives her the look of the Beestung pucker.

Shape of the Brow

There are many parts of an eyebrow to consider when emulating a period look. The inner corner and tail, peak level, thickness along the brow and the length of the brow can determine if the look works for the decade.

Look for descriptions throughout the book of eyebrow shapes considered attractive at the time. Also pay special attention to brow shape when using an old photograph as a reference.

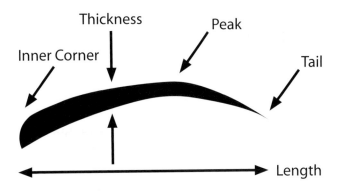

In the images below, the eyebrows of the same model are made to look significantly different with small alterations in shape using makeup. On the brow to the left, the hair is brushed upward and an eyebrow pencil is used to add height and angle to the top of the peak above the brow. Highlight is used below the brow to accentuate the rise of the eyebrow for the look of the 1950s. On the brow to the right, the hair is brushed downward and to the side and a pencil is used below the peak to fill in and straighten the brow for a more 1920s look.

Brow Grooming Products

Pencil

Pencils can provide a very diverse look. A hard pencil sharpened to a perfect point can be used to draw individual hairs into bald brow spots to look like the natural brow or they can be used softly like a powder to fill in larger sections. They are the best for drawing the tail into a perfect point.

Powder and Brush

Brow powder is best for filling in the brows for a soft effect. Often brow powders come in a duo or trio color set so you can control the darkness level by mixing different powders and applying with a heavier or lighter hand. It is best to use powder toward the inner corner of the brow and finish the tail with a pencil for more definition.

Wax/Pomade

Brow wax is the strongest product for controlling hair direction. Available in clear, brown or black, it packs a lot of thickening power. It is best for fine eyebrow hair, adding volume to individual hairs. Mustache wax has much of the same consistency and effect.

Gel

Eyebrow gel comes in a tube and applies with a wand. Either clear or in a natural color, they help in numerous ways by controlling hair, adding volume to fine eyebrow hairs, and deepening color without changing the skin color under the brow.

Shaping

1. Before making a plunge that involves waxing or tweezing, understand that sometimes when you pull hair out at the root, it does not come back. Move forward carefully and with caution.

2. Wild eyebrow hairs that stick out and will not be tamed can be cut past the preferred eyebrow line. Scissors can also help create a blunt eyebrow line. Use them sparingly though.

3. Tweeze the hairs above the brow first so that when you tweeze the lower hairs you have a better visual of how far up you can go.

4. Use a white pencil to draw the lower curve of the desired shape and double check that the brow will be the right shape for you. If the shape works you may begin tweezing the bulk of the hairs that fall within this white pencil mark.

5. Clean the white pencil off with a cotton swab.

6. Tweeze any stray hairs to refine the eyebrow.

Tips - If you draw on the eyebrows and they look too dark, brush your eyebrows heavily with a clean mascara wand removing product gradually to the desired lightness. Also, hairspray or gel on a clean mascara wand can tame unruly eyebrow hair.

Eyelash Curling

The first Kurlash was introduced in 1923. The early form was difficult to use and took minutes to do each eye.[1] By the end of the 1920s, the eyelash curler metamorphosed into what we are more familiar with and has not changed much since.

The best curl is not forced. Start the curl at the base of the lashes as close as you can get without pinching the skin. Lightly close the tongs together. Do not close tightly as this will cause a weird crimp. Hold for a few seconds and then loosen the grip. Repeat as you work your way out on your lashes.

Applying Eyelashes

The first false eyelashes were created for the stage and screen much like fake beards. They were a combination of gauze and human hair.[2]

For the best self application, after you have curled your lashes, dip the lash strip into and run it along the surface of eyelash glue for a light coat. Glue is available in clear or dark, drying black. Allow the glue to dry for a couple of seconds.

Take both ends of the strip in your fingers. Holding your chin up and looking into a wall mirror to open up the lid area, pull the strip slightly taut and hold close to the eyelid above your natural lashes. Slowly lower the lashes, bringing the glue strip to the skin at the base of the natural lashes.

Soak them in warm water for 5 minutes after removal to clean off the glue and reuse.

Lashes Over the Decades

1920s and 1930s
Early false lashes had fewer strands. The points of the long strands were well defined and meant to lengthen rather than thicken.

1940s
For a natural look, lashes with more tapered strands work well to thicken.

1950s
For a more 1950s look, try lashes that taper to the outer corner, creating the doe-eyed effect, or apply a few clusters to the outer corner of the eye.

1960s
False lashes were thick and long, not meant to look at all natural. Often editorial makeup artists applied them in multiples on the same eye. The addition of lashes to the lower lash line became very popular during the 1960s, and can be done with strips or singles.

Mascara

In the 19th century, darkening of the lashes was done with home products like burnt cork[3] or lampblack, the black produced by the flame of a candle held below a ceramic plate.[4] Mascaro, an early predecessor to mascara, was a dye pomade or cake that men used in the 19th century to cover greys in their mustaches and around their temples. Women used it to tint their eyebrows and eyelashes.[5] Mascaro had evolved into mascara by the end of WWI.[6]

Inspired by his sister Maybel, T.L. Williams started Maybell Laboratories in 1915 with the help of drug manufacturer Park-Davis. After Maybel accidentally singed her brows and lashes, Williams watched her use a Vaseline concoction she learned from *Photoplay* magazine to help regrow them.

His first product, Lash-Brow-Ine, was the result and was marketed as a growth promoter. After some new product development, Maybelline was introduced in 1917 as a cake eyelash and eyebrow beautifier.

Application of these early mascaras involved wetting a brush and dabbing it across the cake mascara. In 1957, Helena Rubenstein introduced Mascara-Matic, the first mascara applied with a wand instead of a brush.[7]

Lipstick

Early lipstick came in messy paper wrappers. The first documented metal slide container for lipstick, which was also used for eyebrow and eye shadow pencils, came about in 1915 when Scovill offered lipstick in shades of orange, red and deep rose in these new containers.[8,9] The metal cover made it easy to carry in a handbag,[10] and the first swivel version of the metal container was patented in 1923 by James Mason Jr.[11]

Lip brushes, although used in the movie industry very early on, were not offered to consumers until 1929, when Max Factor released his first commercial lip brush. Max Factor was selling a lipstick pencil by 1940.[12]

Lipstick that Lasts

For a longer lasting application, try these steps.

1. First apply a light layer of foundation and powder over lips. This helps to create a blank canvas if you are under or over-drawing lips for a retro shape.
2. Using a dull point lip liner of choice, draw the desired lip shape. The color underneath the lipstick directly effects the color above. If you want to get the lipstick to the right color, use the proper lip liner color underneath.
3. If any mistakes are made on the outer edge, place a cotton swab directly outside the lip and wipe inward.
4. Fill in the lips with the same lip liner.
5. Carefully clean any difficult edges with foundation. Use a triangle sponge to powder at the edge of the lip line to help prevent bleed.
6. Apply lipstick with a lip brush. It is easier to control color application and follow the lip line that was so carefully drawn than with just straight lipstick application.
7. You can matte the lips more and prevent smearing by peeling one ply off of a tissue. Place it lightly over the lips and powder over with a translucent powder.

Red Lip Product Options

Lipstick

Lipstick offers the deepest color and most coverage.

Lip Gloss

Lip gloss can get messy since it is not made for staying power, but it is a good option for girls uncomfortable with painted lips.

Lip Stain

Stains are great because you can build up the application to the color density you want. Staining the lips was very popular during the early 1900s.

Understanding the Color Lingo

Someone can be told what the right red lipstick shade is for their coloring, but until the color variations in red are fully understood, it does not do much good. Understand also that lipstick partially takes on the lip color or lip liner shade underneath. With natural pink lips, the red lipstick will look cooler, so be sure to try it before you buy it.

    Cool toned reds are reds that have more blue/purple in them and less yellow/orange. Using the lipstick shades below, the color balance starts in #1 with a cool pink that has no orange or yellow to speak of. A deeper version of this is #2 in a more cherry color. With color #3, added warmth brings the red to a true red, equal parts of magenta and yellow. As blue is removed and yellow added, that color warms up to coral in #5, and finally, a light tawny orange in #6.

1   2   3   4   5   6

The undertone of skin is the greatest factor in choosing a red lipstick.

For a yellow undertone:
1. Since yellow and red are analogous colors, a true red harmonizes well.
2. Warm Red with warm skin is the most pleasing and soft option. The colors do not contrast with each other.
3. Try deep cherry red for a dramatic statement.

For an olive undertone:
This skin type has the most freedom in color choice, but it is best to stick with saturated colors for emphasis.
1. A basic red is tame on darker skin for the daytime.
2. Deep plum adds more drama for a less bubble gum feel if you are going for the 1920s or '30s look.
3. Bright ruby red works well for evening. It still appears bright under dim lighting

For bronze skin:
Bronze skin can be tricky. A true bronze is a warm neutral in color, but neutral does not mean everything goes with it.
1. For a softer look, a rose, very popular throughout the 20th century, provides just enough color without being overpowering.
2. A tawny orange coordinates well with the warmth of the skin, hazel eyes, and warm blonde hair.
3. For drama, a red with extra yellow undertones is great.

For skin that has a very pale yellow surface, but rosy flush underneath (top image set):
1. This is a cooler skin tone and a cool red with a hint of pink looks healthy, not washed out.
2. A coral pink is appropriate for period makeup for a day look.
3. Wear deep cherry red for the evening.

For a warm redhead:
Although redheads can have cool complexions, the warmth of the hair overwhelms and the lipstick should harmonize.
1. Wear brick red for everyday.
2. Tawny orange lipstick was very popular for a redhead in the 1940s.
3. A dark cherry red is good for a darker look.

For a pale blue undertone:
1. A true red, equal parts red and yellow, is best. Blue red makes a blue-skinned woman appear grey and unhealthy.
2. A rose lipstick matches closely with the blue undertones without washing out the skin.
3. A light plum is a good alternative to dark. Too dark and the skin looks pasty.

The 1920s

During the Roaring Twenties the use of face paint was still very new. While some women were trying to learn how to properly apply it, other women were trying to banish it. The latter introduced a bill in Kansas, attempting to make it a misdemeanor for anyone under the age of forty-four to wear cosmetics "for the purpose of creating a false impression."[1] Girls shocked their parents with painted lips in increasingly vivid colors.[2]

The flappers, influenced by movies, jazz and dance, were flaunting their use of makeup. Gone were the days of hiding away in the ladies room to touch-up. Women pulled their compacts out in public at the restaurant table or on the dance floor and reapplied with pride. The flapper wanted everyone to notice her bob, her dress and her painted face.[3]

Along with this new fashion also came inexperience. Ladies used movie stars and magazines to teach them proper application, because they certainly could not learn it from their mothers. It was a great development period for makeup style and could also be a great disaster. "All girls were adjured to do the same thing, so that we can remember whole eras like the nose-in-the-flower barrel, the twin-sunsets-on-cheeks, the corpse-face with the scarlet gash for a mouth, the recent mahogany finish all over..." *Colliers*, 1931.[4]

Launched in 1924, Kleenex was a solution to a surplus of lightweight cotton wadding. Paper manufacturer Kimberly-Clark developed this "creped" wadding for a consumer product it developed called Kotex. The feminine hygiene product was not accepted by consumers at the time, so the company reformulated the ingredients to make it softer. The development team marketed this disposable cleansing tissue to women as a replacement for the "cold cream towel" hanging in their bathroom.[5]

"If you still use a soiled bit of linen that rubs germs back into the skin or a harsh towel that is so quickly ruined by cream and grease, you'll find Kleenex a delightful surprise...You use Kleenex once, then discard it just like paper."
1928 Advertisement [6]

Cosmetic sales boomed in the 1920s. By 1921, they had risen to $52 million, half a billion dollars by today's standards.[7] According to a 1928 article in the *Milwaukee Sentinel*, consumers had a choice of 1300 different face powders (the most common cosmetic, used by 90% of women), 1200 perfumes, and 347 rouge varieties (used by only half of the women polled). The same article claimed only 15% of women were using lipstick.[8]

Many of these cosmetics were not necessarily color altering products. The cosmetic industry offered beautifiers whose purposes were to improve the appearance of a healthy complexion such as vanishing creams (named for vanishing upon application) and skin foods. Among the color altering cosmetics you might find on a woman's vanity were:

Mascara, most often black, came in cake form. The brush applicator was wetted with water and the brush scraped along the mascara cake before being applied to the lashes.

Face Powder came in a variety of colors and was the main product used for cover-up.

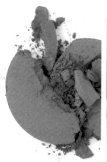

Eyeliner, most often in brown or black, was used for many purposes. It was considered appropriate to apply a light amount along the upper eyelid at the base of the lashes. It could also be used to lightly color in the eyebrows. Pencils came in other colors also, like blue and violet. For a hint of eye shadow, a woman applied a colored eyeliner and blotted with her finger to spread and blend on her eyelid.

Rouge came in a powder compact, paste or cream form. Powders came with a small flat puff for application and fingers were used for paste and cream application.

Eye Shadow application was done lightly with the finger at the lash line and blended up toward the brow. Women did not have wands or brushes that came with their eye shadow. In fact, very rarely did a woman have a makeup brush of any kind for precision application. A lot of women did not even have toothbrushes during the decade, let alone makeup brushes.[9]

Lipstick, available at the time but most often worn by young women or in the evening, was gaining acceptance quickly. Women also used colored lip salves and pomades for color.

Early Foundation

The term foundation comes from the original use of liquid base cosmetics in the early part of the 20th century. Although they were not always translucent, sometimes with a pink or nude tint, they were not often meant to do the job of coloring the skin.

These lotions and creams were applied to the skin first. Their purpose was to create the base or foundation for a powder to stick to, much like a face primer today. Powder provided the color and coverage to achieve the desired skin tone.

Some heavier foundations existed in the movie industry, but in the 1920s the general public did not use them.

To achieve a more authentic 1920s foundation base, apply a face moisturizer or faint tinted moisturizer with an SPF for good measure. Then follow with a loose powder in the desired skin tone.

"If you wish a certain feature to seem more prominent, then attract attention to it through color." The Art of Makeup, Tangee 1930[10]

A very common belief in makeup theory in the early 20th century was that rouge was to be applied to what you wanted to bring attention to. For instance, on a long face apply the rouge color to be deeper below the cheekbone. The concept was that putting color there would make the face appear wider by drawing focus there. If your face was wide, rouge should be higher on the cheek and closer to the nose.

The concept is sound. This would bring attention to the areas where there is more color, but unlike contouring, would not make the face appear any wider or thinner. It, in fact, probably had the opposite effect since, as explained in contouring, adding darkness makes areas recede.

Eyebrow and Lip Shapes

The most popular eyebrow shape of the 1920s was a long, thin brow colored in with either a brown or black pencil. Not to be confused with the shaved off and drawn-back-on brow of the 1930s, this brow still used the natural hairs as guidance.

The thickness was generally equal along the entire length of the brow. The inner corner was high and there was no defined peak like the brows of the 1950s. The 1920s brow arch was an even graduation, sometimes following the brow bone and sometimes drawn to mimic the shape of the top part of the eye.

Other less common shapes included a thicker version of the first eyebrow. It still came to a thin long point that coincided with the point of the outer corner of the eye. A short, flat brow worn by a few actresses was also popular.

Generally, the lip shape of the 1920s was a thin lip. Women often under-drew their lips to keep them from looking too round and wide. It was more about creating attention and less about full, sensuous lips. Tangee told women the proper way to apply their lipstick should start, "at the center of the upper lip. Make a curve upward and outward. Finish a bit short of the corner."[11]

The Beestung lip shape started its reign when movie makeup artists were having trouble with lip pomades. Under the hot movie lights, the makeup would melt into the corner of the actresses' mouths and into their face makeup. It became necessary to keep the lipstick centered on the lips and away from the corners.

During the late 1920s, when talkies started, this look no longer worked with the opening and closing of the mouth. The next step was still similar to the beestung, but the shape was drawn out thinly and stopped just shy of the inner corner of the mouth. This shape was named the Cupid's Bow.[12]

Coloring of the 1920s

Cosmetics was a product-driven industry. A woman had few options for making herself up if she did not purchase a product. Because makeup was so new and manufacturers wanted women to buy into the beauty they were selling, companies produced multitudes of information on application. Women needed to know what to do with their new fashionable faces.

The booklet *The New Art of Society Makeup,* produced by Max Factor in 1928, provided women with his color formulas that he himself used on his movie star clients.

For most of the 1920s and into the '30s, the color options suggested to women were based heavily on their own coloring. A certain eye color should wear a certain shade of shadow, a certain hair color should be accompanied with a certain color powder. As the years progressed, experts' advice included the matching of makeup with the clothing worn.

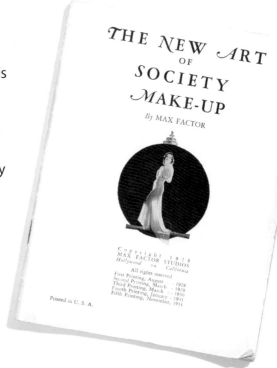

THE NEW ART OF SOCIETY MAKE-UP

By MAX FACTOR

Copyright 1928
MAX FACTOR STUDIOS
Hollywood California

All rights reserved

First Printing, August 1928
Second Printing, March 1929
Third Printing, March 1929
Fourth Printing, January 1930
Fifth Printing, November 1931

Printed in U. S. A.

For Blue Eyes

Grey or Blue Eye Shadow
Brown Eyeliner
Brown Mascara

For Green Eyes

Grey or Green Eye Shadow
Brown Eyeliner
Brown Mascara

For Brown Eyes

Brown or Plum Eye Shadow
Black Eyeliner
Black Mascara

Other suggestions included, "With blue eyes, a blue or purple eyebrow pencil may be used to shade the lids, while brown or hazel eyes demand a purple pencil to develop their full beauty. Black eyes are lovely with a faint touch of red. Rub the pencil very gently over the eyelids and blend into a delicate shadow over the entire surface." *Sunset Magazine*, 1926.[13] This article also suggested that it may be appropriate to add a very small amount of shadowing to the lower lid and blending it to be indistinct.

In 1929, Maybelline added eyeliners, eyebrow pencils and eye shadows to their product line. Eyebrow pencils were brown and black. Eye shadows were blue, black, brown and green. The company added violet eye shadow in 1930.[14]

When it came to the color of the skin, in the very early 1920s, pale was in, but that changed quickly when the fashion of the tan took hold. *Nation* in 1923 suggested to women, "...match your powder to your skin. Nature knew what she was doing."[15] In 1925, Henry Telow observed that women in Europe preferred powders with a warmer tint like *Rachel* or *Cream*, but in America, pink shades were most popular.[16]

Tangee's formula for powder for the skin was *Flesh* for a blonde, *Rachel* for the true brunette, *Cream* for the mid-brunette and *Tan* for the Summer girl.

Tangee lipstick came into fashion at this time and is still available today. The sales pitch for the brand was that the color would change to suit its wearer's specific color needs. It started out as orange in the tube and changed to an intense pink on the lips. This supposed "natural" blending made it much easier for parents to accept their teen daughters wearing it.

The science behind it was not based on the skin tone of the wearer, though. The lipstick contained the dye bromo-acid which changed based on the alkaline content of the surface of the lips.[17] For twenty cents, a girl could get a miniature size of the lipstick and a booklet on *The Art of Makeup* full of tips on the proper application and use of Tangee products.[18]

In the early 1920s, rouge was sometimes a little more garish, like tangerine orange, poppy reds and carmine reds. For most of the decade raspberry blush was available, and in the later part of the decade rose rouge became the fashion.

Lipstick color often followed along with the colors of rouge. Tangerine was popular, but fell mostly out of fashion by the end of the decade. Reds were the most prominent, but also plums, warm reds, and later on, lighter colors like rose and pink. The color-changing Tangee, which turned pink on the lips, was a very popular brand throughout the decade.

Sadie

Inspired by movie star and fashion icon Gloria Swanson, these steps are simple ways to bring out the very defined, angular lines popular in her makeup style. Her piercing stare with these defined lines added strength to her many dramatic roles in silent films.

1. Model Amber's natural eyebrows are fine and light in color. A brow gel is used to direct the hair to the side and make the brow appear flatter. This also thickens and darkens the hair.

2. A sharp eyebrow pencil in a similar color to the gel is then used to lengthen the eyebrow out to a fine point that slightly droops on the outer corner.

3. A shimmer eye shadow in a neutral light color is washed on the entire upper eyelid.

4. A brown-black eyeliner is drawn onto the lash line in a fine line to thicken the appearance of the

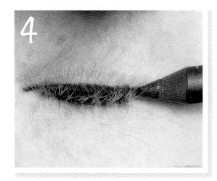

lashes. Plain black eyeliner would diminish the depth of the eye makeup.

5. Using a fine-pointed smudging brush, apply a dark brown shimmer eye shadow along the line drawn with the eyeliner and smudge the shadow into the line to create a shiny brown smoky eye.

6. Apply a pop of color to sit on the apples of the cheeks and just below. Lips are thin, but the lower lip should be only slightly thicker for a pouty look. (See page 24 for tips on lipstick application.)

7. Finish with black mascara and a beauty mark below the outer corner of the lips. (See page 50 for more directions on beauty marks.)

Decorative Knee Painting

"Her skirt was short, her stockings neatly rolled, and-if you please-two highly colored landscapes were painted on her knees!" Carolyn Wells verse for a Nell Brinkley Cartoon, *The American Weekly*, February 7, 1926.

A fad for flapper girls in the 1920s involved rolling down their stockings and painting shapes on their knees. These various designs could be stripes, flowers, leaves, birds, and other simple scenes of nature.[19]

Lulu

Actress Louise Brooks epitomized flapper style. Her dark lips and kohl black liner brought out the attitude of the trouble maker she portrayed in *Pandora's Box.* **Her flat eyebrows that almost raise at the outside of the corners of her eyes help to raise her mischievous appearance.**

1. Eyebrows are brushed to the side to flatten their appearance and eyebrow gel in brown thickens and darkens the hair.

2. Most eyebrows naturally droop down at the outer corner. For this look, you can either remove the hair at the outer corner below the brow bone by shaving, cover with the eyebrow cover steps laid out on page 51, or use a thick concealer to lighten the hairs by coating them. Although this does not make them disappear, it provides a good temporary option.

3. Using a dark eyebrow pencil, fill in below the arch to flatten the eyebrow appearance. Draw the eyebrow straight out at the outer corner.

4. With a black eyeliner, draw a fine line around the entire eye. The point at the outer corner of the eye should come straight out.

5. Using a smudging brush and a charcoal eye shadow, smudge the liner slightly to soften the lines.

6. The cupid's bow of the upper lip is well defined into points with an even drop from the peak of the points to the outer corners of the mouth, as opposed to a droop or a wide round descent. If the lower lip is naturally larger, under-draw with the lip liner to achieve a thinner lower lip. (Use the steps on page 24 to aid in lipstick application.)

Some Lesser-known Fads

Some lesser-known makeup fads in the 1920s included rouging the earlobes when you wore your hair back and leaving a strip of bare lip down the middle of the top lip. Inspired by stage performers, girls were also encouraged to rouge their fingertips and palms for a night out on the town or to bead their lashes, a process that involved either building wax into balls at the ends the lashes or applying mascara heavily to bead up.[20]

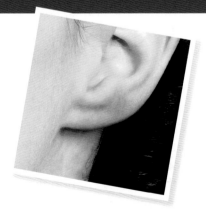

Bronze Venus

It is Josephine Baker's sensational, sensual dancing in theatres in France that she is most known for today, but she was also an actress, singer, muse and activist. Everything about her appearance went above and beyond. Her costumes, her jewelry and her makeup all added to her fantastic performance and inspired artists such as Pablo Picasso and Christian Dior. Her large eyes with heavy makeup inspired this makeup look.

1. Draw the eyebrows in dark for this look. The eyebrows should be thin to medium thickness and long and flat in shape.

2. Using an eye shadow brush, apply a brown shimmer eye shadow all over the upper eyelid.

3. Apply a thick black line of eyeliner around the entire eye. The corners of the eyeliner are drawn slightly out to elongate the eye shape.

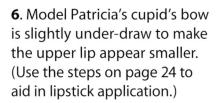

4. With a mixture of deep plum shimmer and charcoal eye shadow and a smudging brush, blend the eyeliner around the entire eye. Baker's eye makeup was often very thick and dark, especially when she was in her stage costumes.

5. Reapply more black eyeliner at the lash line. Baker's lashes were thick and coated in mascara, and she often beaded her lashes. To mimic the effect, false lashes coated in mascara with the tips bluntly cut have been used.

6. Model Patricia's cupid's bow is slightly under-draw to make the upper lip appear smaller. (Use the steps on page 24 to aid in lipstick application.)

Healthy Glow?

Marie Curie and her husband discovered the element radium in 1898. Since it was not widely known at the time how dangerous it was, even in small doses (in fact killing Madame Curie over time), manufacturers were quick to mix it into any number of products sold to the public, touting its healing properties. An advertisement for Radior Toilet Requisites claimed "When scientists discovered Radium they hardly dreamed they had unearthed a revolutionary 'Beauty Secret.' They know it now. Radium Rays vitalize and energize all living tissue." The Tho-Radia brand was a French company partly owned by a Dr. Alfred Curie who was probably brought on as a name maker since he had no relation to *the* Curies.[21]

Promoted as "the girl with the most beautiful face in Hollywood," Anita Page had a short, but successful film career. Her eyes were shaded heavily toward the nose to enhance the shape. This was done very often with makeup on movie stars during the 1920s to suggest the look of almost an innocent child.

1. To make eyebrows appear thinner, use your thumb placed above the eyebrow and an eyebrow wand below the eyebrow and press the hair in between them with light pressure toward the center of the line of the eyebrow.

2. Apply a wash of a nude eye shadow over the entire lid.

3. With a medium brown eye shadow create a shape on the eyelid that starts high on the

inner section of the eyelid and slowly drops in height toward the outer corner of the eyelid.

4. With a slightly darker shade of brown eye shadow, deepen the color toward the inner part of the upper eyelid.

5. Using a small smudging brush, blend a medium brown eye shadow just at the lash line on the lower eyelid. Finish with black mascara.

6. Add a light pop of red blush on the apples of the cheeks and blend.

7. Use the steps below in *Options for Retro Lip Coloring* for the lips.

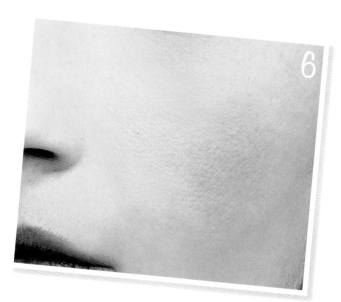

Option for Retro Lip Coloring

Lip coloring was not always a heavy painted look. Max Factor, after developing his lip gloss in the late 1920s, released the lip gloss *X-Rated* in 1932.[22] Staining was a very popular lip color option as far back as ancient Egypt. In the very early 1900s, it was a more acceptable form of lip color. For a stain look today, try applying a clear lip gloss on your lips, then a red lipstick over it for a sheer lip coverage.

Popularizing the Tan

"Just a nice, comfortable, careless tan is what every woman ought to have in Summer if she wants to help her skin all she can. It is becoming to nearly everyone in light summer clothes and it is good for the skin." Celia Caroline Cole, *Delineator*, 1919.

Double MONEY-BACK Guarantee

Tan WITH Gaby

• NO ALCOHOL TO DRY YOUR SKIN
• NO OIL TO FRY YOUR SKIN

10¢ · 25¢
50¢ · $1.00
At toilet and cosmetic counters and 5 and 10c stores

BLONDES! BRUNETTES! RED HEADS!

Why suffer the misery of sunburn and blistering... when you can tan beautifully, easily, with Gaby? This sincere, unqualified guarantee is only made because millions have used Gaby and have found it dependable! Try Gaby... if it doesn't block out harmful sunrays and promote a beautiful tan return the unused portion to Gaby, Philadelphia, Pa., and we'll cheerfully refund double the purchase price!

Pleasant Odor · Not Sticky

Gaby
GREASELESS SUNTAN LOTION

Prior to and into the 1920s, it was considered delicate and beautiful to be pale. Going back to ancient times, women who were wealthy had pale skin thanks to their leisure activities indoors. If you were a peasant, you were probably out in the fields or tending to your own garden and getting some color in the process.

Hence, for thousands of years, the look of pale skin was considered the ideal. Parasols were popular and women tried bleaching agents and lightening home remedies galore to get the look of pale skin. In 1921, *Vogue* recommended a method "for removing tan and other blemishes." It involved a bleach applied to the face, neck and arms, then removal, application of a less powerful bleach and removal, finished with a "delicious skin food."[23]

Pale powder makeup was the popular color choice, and honestly, about the only choice. The powders came in delicate variations in color from pink to peach to yellow, but they were mostly pale. White was also an option, but by the mid-1920s it was considered special to use it. In 1923, *Nation* recommends "...dead white if you want to be bizarre."

Beginning in the early 20th century, something very subtle happened. The way a woman got sun on her skin changed and so did her attitude toward its beauty.

She no longer got a tan from work. The working woman was now in the factory or in the department store away from the sun. The leisurely vacationing woman was playing tennis or golf, sunning on the beach and skiing on the slopes. Public swimming pools were popping up all over thanks to New

Deal social programs in the 1930s. Athletic was in and so was the tan you got in participating.[24]

In 1929, a manufacturer sold 200,000 bottles of an instant tan product in ten days.[25] At first, cosmetics manufacturers were caught off guard by the high demand of this new love of the sun.[26] Once they recognized the demand though, manufacturers realized the products that this new skin treatment required were endless.

In 1924, Jean Parou introduced the sun lotion Huile de Caldee for darkening your tan. In 1928, Dorothy Gray's Sunburn Cream, containing benzyl salicylate and benzyl cinnamate, was developed as a sunscreen.[27] Thanks to developments in electricity and light bulbs, companies like General Electric developed single lamp tanning devices for the home.

Makeup also developed around this new skin coloring. Elizabeth Arden sold Velva Beauty Film, similar to a liquid foundation, to give the appearance of a tan. It could be applied all over the body.

Helena Rubenstein also recognized the importance of "foundation lotions and films that give the skin a golden tan."[28] Her recommendation for a sun tan makeup was, "a dark foundation, a lighter shade of powder, brilliant rouge and lipstick. Emphasize eyes with brown or black mascara and much eye-shadow. Brighten your eyelids with cream or oil."[29]

The colors of cosmetics for tanned skin included tawny or orange lipstick and rouge. Rouge was down played for the tanned skin, but you could add a little rouge on the chest where sunburn would normally appear. Pink and white powders were replaced with warm, dark powders. These powders either matched the newly tanned skin or added a tanned effect much like bronzers today.[30]

TAN gloriously! Use SKOL

For a glorious tan without ugly, painful sunburn, use . . . SKOL! SKOL filters out the harmful burning rays, but lets the tanning rays pass through! SKOL is not greasy, doesn't pick up sand, dries quickly. Contains an exclusive, patented form of tannic acid. SKOL is antiseptic, helps *relieve* sunburn too. Pleasant to use. SKOL Company, Inc., New York.

NON-OILY

SKOL — PREVENTS PAINFUL SUNBURN · BLENDS & DIRECTS THE TAN · COATING NO OILY SKINS

QUICK-DRYING · ANTISEPTIC · PLEASANT TO USE

PREVENTS PAINFUL SUNBURN!

Home tanning lotion[31]
  1/4 ounce cider vinegar
  2 ounces caron oil
  1 1/2 ounces iodine
  1/2 ounce baby oil
  4 ounces favorite cologne

The 1930s

The Great Depression did not have the negative effect on cosmetic sales one might expect. It was an affordable luxury during tough times and sales actually rose significantly between 1929 and 1930. A woman could not afford a new dress, but she could afford a new lipstick.[1]

Makeup had become common now. Magazines were offering more and more guidance on proper use of cosmetics. Thanks to cosmetic companies providing a lot of revenue, magazines had no problem extending editorial content about the products in these advertisements.[2] There was also no lack of subjects to write about in the cosmetic industry.

The Vanity

On a lady's vanity in the 1930s you might find any of these face and nail cosmetic products and tools.[3]

- Cleansing/cold creams
- Astringent like witch hazel
- Skin tonic
- Skin food
- Foundation/vanishing cream
- Cake foundations toward the end of the decade
- Powder (colors for day or evening, winter or summer)
- Eye shadow
- Tweezers
- Eyebrow/eyeliner pencil
- Eyelash curler
- Mascara cake
- Rouge (colors for day and evening)
- Lipstick (colors for day and evening)
- Lip brush
- Hand lotion
- Nail bleach
- Nail whitening pencil
- Nail polish
- Nail polish remover
- Nail care kit containing an orangewood stick, metal file, emery board, cuticle snippers, nail brush and buffer

In the 1930s, color options had grown and popular shapes were different, but the basic product application of makeup had not changed significantly. Powder, rouge, eye shadow, mascara, eyeliner and lipstick were in regular use. Foundations were becoming more popular.

Of the major developments of the time was Max Factor's introduction of Pan-Cake in 1937, a foundation cover-up in cake form. Color films were in desperate need of a new foundation since previous paints for black and white films were reproducing horribly in color.

What Factor did not anticipate were the models appearing in the movie *Vogues,* the first movie to officially use Pan-Cake, loving it so much that they were stealing it from the set to wear in everyday life. He had to work fast to meet the unprecedented demand for the new makeup.

It caught on quickly and other cosmetic companies started producing their own cake form foundations, such as Elizabeth Arden's Pat-A-Kake (later changed after trademark disputes). Within months, there were 65 competitors producing cake foundations.[4]

Thanks to this new development in makeup,

"...women everywhere became uniformly flat."[5]

Also, the lip brush was gaining popularity. Women still carried their lipstick in their tubes, but with the changing lip shapes, the brush made reshaping into lips such as Joan Crawford's Hunter's Bow much easier.

Eyebrow and Lip Shapes

The greatest change in the design of the popular eyebrow shape was the arch. Still thin and long like the 1920s eyebrow, the '30s difference was that the brow now ascended into a rounded peak that ended in a fine point.

"Eyebrows should not grow down on the concave side of the eye socket. Nor should eyebrows grow in...points toward the forehead." Virginia Vincent, 1932.[6]

Lip size increased for the 1930s, but still followed basic lip size and shape. The lip was well defined. Women were no longer under-drawing for a thin lip and, with the influence of women like Hedy Lamarr and Joan Crawford, over-drawing was coming into style. The peaks of the upper lip were kept rounded.

Lipstick was available in both matte and shine. In 1938, Volupte introduced two lipsticks to the public. The lighter colored *Lady* was a "soft mat finish", while the deeper *Hussy* provided "a gleaming lustre." *Hussy* outsold *Lady* five to one.[7]

A few actresses had their own special shapes that they made into fads. The most notable eyebrows came about in the 1930s. Actresses like Claudette Colbert and Jean Harlow shaved their eyebrows off completely to redraw an exaggerated, arched line high above the natural brow bone. The lines varied in angle, arch, width and length between different women.

To change her image, Joan Crawford started wearing the Hunter's Bow. Max Factor called it The Smear because the lipstick was smeared outside the natural lip line. In contrast to the Cupid's Bow from the 1920s with its small curve in the center, the Hunter's Bow takes the length from the center dip of the upper lip all the way out to the outer corner of the lip to make its full curve. Although not many women went as huge as The Smear, the wide curves did catch on and many actresses and women followed suit.

Powder

Well into the 1940s beautiful skin was expected to be shine free. There were special occasions for sheen added to the eyes, but the most becoming look for the skin was matte. By the 1940s, 90% of women used face powder, in loose or compact form.[8]

One application process brought to consumers from the theatre and movie industry started with over powdering the skin to be sure to get powder into each crevice of the face. Then, a special soft brush was used to brush away the excess powder.

The Mystery of Rachel

Of the cosmetic color names used in the early 20th century, nothing is more perplexing than the powder called *Rachel*. It is listed in books of the time and every makeup company had the color in their line. Companies used a lot of creativity in naming lipstick and nail polish for uniqueness, but *Rachel* was a staple in the cosmetic arsenal.

The color was actually a peaches and creme color, on the warmer side of the color spectrum. So why did they call it *Rachel*?

The name had been around since the middle of the 1800s. At the time, French actress Elisa Rachel Felix took the stage name Rachel. She was widely acclaimed for both her beauty and talent. She also died at an early age of tuberculosis, which further sealed her reputation for endless beauty.

Since stage makeup at the time was powder, the name was picked up for a particular shade of powder, probably the one she wore, and continued on into the 1950s.[9]

Coloring and Application of the 1930s

Much like the 1920s, the colors recommended to women were based highly on their natural coloring, but could also be subject to the occasion or the costume.

If basing the eye shadow color on the color of the eyes:

Blue Eyes
- Mixture of grey and blue eye shadow
- Blue iridescent eye shadow topped with blue-green, blue or brown mascara
- Combination of blue with a hint of dark green eye shadow
- Mauve eye shadow
- For evening, an eye shadow with a hint of gold or silver

Green and Hazel Eyes
- Green or greenish-blue eye shadow
- Dark blue eye shadow
- Purple eye shadow with iridescent gold
- Brown mascara and eyebrow pencil

Brown Eyes
- Purple eye shadow with deep purple mascara
- Blue-green eye shadow
- Brown eye shadow with black mascara
- A combination of violet and gold eye shadow

Other times the color decision could be based on a lady's clothing. Betty Thornley Stuart in *Colliers* in 1931 told women that if the outfit is blue, "Your eyes should be made up with a neutral light brown creme eye shadow, applied all over the entire lid from lash to brow, shaded a bit with dark blue, outward on the lid and toward the corner." If the outfit is green, the same recipe should be followed, but with a green shadow.[10]

In *This Way to Beauty*, Helena Rubenstein recommended Chinese red rouge and lipstick for a black or brilliant red outfit. For white, wear geranium rouge and lipstick, and yellow clothing goes well with poppy red rouge and lipstick. Grey or green clothing should be accompanied by coral red; beige or brown outfits go well with terra cotta makeup; and blue, purple or wine clothing goes with red velvet or raspberry lipstick.

The general consensus included that makeup was to be lighter during the day, including colored lip pomades or lighter lipsticks, and that rouge and lipstick should at least be a similar color. Eyeshadow could be left alone or a small amount applied on the upper lid for just a hint of color. Mascara was an option for darkening the eyebrows, much like a brow gel today.

More Recommendations

Marlene Dietrich never applied mascara to her lower lashes because she thought it produced an unbecoming shadow.[11] It was not common to apply liner on the lower eyelid, but for evenings, you could apply a Persian eyeblack around the entire eye with the index finger covered in linen.[12] Another evening look from Rubenstein was the application of an eye shadow the color of your eyes on the lower part of the top lid and an iridescent shadow blended up to the eyebrows.

In May of 1930, *Harper's Bazaar* reported on Peggy Sage's introduction of a line of products in which the lipstick and nail polish match each other, available in *Lido Crimson*, *Riviera Red* and *Palm Beach Coral*.[13] Rubenstein also recommended polish and lipstick to match in 1937, and evening lipstick should be darker, such as red velvet or raspberry. In 1938, Shiaparelli's new autumn lipstick colors included *Shiap*, a bright yellowish red; *Incarnate*, a true red; *Fragile*, a bluish pink; *Shocking*, an intense pink; and *Prunaeu*, the color of crushed plums.[14] Blended lipstick could be used as a rouge in a pinch or when money was tight, which also helped a lady match her rouge with her lips.

A Spanish brunette could use a black pencil to extend the outer corner of the eye. The line was to be blended after drawing.[15] Not to be confused with the wing makeup of the 1950s and '60s, this extension was kept low on the corner much like Delores del Rio.

"French women have a clever trick of covering the tip of an orangewood stick with cotton, dipping it into dark powder and gently drawing it along the crease at the corners of the eyes; this gives the eyes an exotic look," wrote Helena Rubenstein. For the Asian eye, she suggested applying a brown or black eye shadow to emphasize skin coloring.

Eyelid Shine

"A slight touch of Vaseline instead of eye-shadow may be used on the eyelid to give a 'moist' appearance," advised Virginia Vincent in 1932.[16]
1. For the best results, first apply a nude shadow. Since the shadow will shift, colored shadow will create an unattractive crease mark.
2. Dab a very light coat of Vaseline or baby oil with your finger onto the entire lid.
3. Use a cotton swab to remove excess. This helps keep it from getting too messy for longer wear.

For the look without the Vaseline mess, find a shiny eye shadow that closely resembles the undertone of your own skin. For yellow undertones, use gold. For a rosy complexion, use a pale shiny rose color.

Beauty Mark

A handful of actresses wore beauty marks in the 1920s and by the '30s, Jean Harlow made them very popular. During the 1940s, the minimal makeup style made a mark overdone, but it made a come back in the '50s.

The beauty mark can be used to cover a blemish or bring attention to your best asset, such as high cheeks or a pretty mouth.

For a long-lasting, natural looking mark, start with an eyeliner pencil in the color of your choice. For emphasis you may use black, but also consider brown or blonde for the day or if very pale. **1.** With the pencil sharpened to a dull point and pointing directly at the skin, mark the location by spinning the pencil. This creates a controlled round dot. **2.** With a fine point brush apply a liquid eyeliner or wet eye shadow to darken and allow to dry.

1

2

Eyebrow Cover

Many costume stores carry the products needed for an eyebrow cover.

One thing to consider is the more coarse the hair in an eyebrow, the more difficult it is to cover. To make a smooth skin-like surface with this method is not easy. There will almost always be a very small amount of texture, but it is a great option for a short-term look. Prosthetic eyebrow covers or hair removal are the best option for a completely smooth effect.

Do not tweeze or wax your eyebrows off completely. For a long-term look, it is best to shave the hairs off. Jean Harlow shaved her brow bone, but many girls in the 1930s tweezed off their brows to look like Harlow or Dietrich, and the hair never grew back.

1. Cover eyebrow hair with spirit gum, a glue made to use on the skin.

2. With a clean mascara wand comb hair flat against skin. Allow to dry.

3. Eyebrow waxes come in various forms. Used here is a stick form. Smear the wax over the brow several times and then use the warmth of your finger to smooth more.

4. The hair at the inner corner sticks out away from the skin most, so use a small ball of wax to pile a little more extra wax there and blend into the surrounding area.

5. Use your finger to smooth and remove excess wax. Do not use your nails. They will dig into the wax too deeply.

6. Cover with a thick concealer that is close to the color of what the finished skin color should be.

7. Apply foundation all over skin and powder. When you are ready to remove, baby oil works well to dissolve spirit gum.

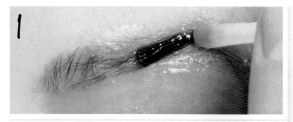

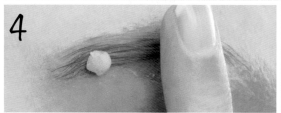

The Platinum Blonde

The eyebrows of Jean Harlow set a very popular trend for movie actresses in the 1930s. The specific purpose of shaving her brows and redrawing them so high and thin was to add balance to her face. Her fair skin and platinum hair were so monochromatic she needed to add heavy makeup to counterbalance.

The two best options to get the appearance of a hairless brow is either to shave the eyebrows or use the eyebrow cover steps on page 51. Do not tweeze or wax your eyebrows off completely. They may not grow back.

1. After you have achieved the hairless-looking brow bone, use a cream makeup or eyebrow pencil to first map out the shape of the desired brow with dots.

2. With a sharp eyebrow pencil or cream

makeup and a fine pointed eyeliner brush, draw the desired eyebrow shape in.

3. If a cream makeup is used, set the line with a fine dark powder and a thin angled eyeliner brush.

4. Apply a matte grey-blue eye shadow at the bottom of the upper eyelid and blend lightly up to the brow bone.

5. With a thin eyeliner brush, apply a fine line of liquid eyeliner at the base of the eyelashes on the upper lid. Do not apply to the lower eyelid. Finish with a strip of false lashes using dark-toned eyelash glue and a coat of mascara.

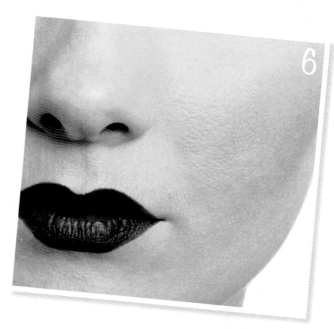

6. Apply a cool raspberry blush to the apples of the cheeks. The cupid's bow of the lips is exaggerated into a heart shape and the lower lip continues the bottom of the heart shape rounded out. (Refer to page 24 for tips on lipstick application.)

7. Harlow's beauty mark often changed positions. (Refer page 50 for more information on creating a beauty mark.)

Some Lesser-known Fads

Because rouge was used as a way to bring emphasis to areas, it was recommended that a dot of rouge be placed at the inner corner of the eye if your eyes were too far apart.[17] Brunettes, in the evening, were encouraged to add mascara to their hairline to bring out the oval of their face.[18]

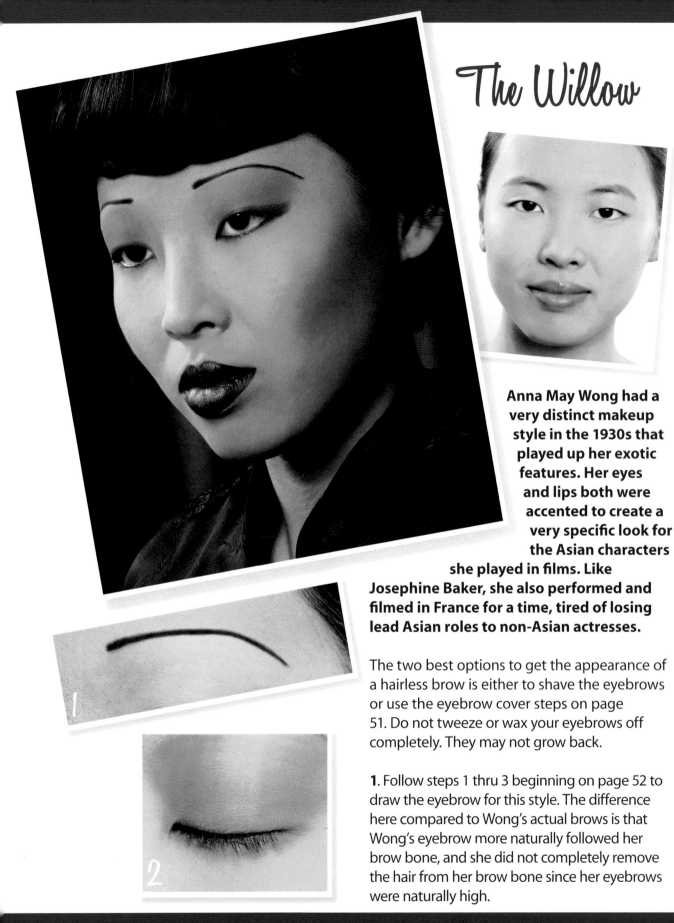

The Willow

Anna May Wong had a very distinct makeup style in the 1930s that played up her exotic features. Her eyes and lips both were accented to create a very specific look for the Asian characters she played in films. Like Josephine Baker, she also performed and filmed in France for a time, tired of losing lead Asian roles to non-Asian actresses.

The two best options to get the appearance of a hairless brow is either to shave the eyebrows or use the eyebrow cover steps on page 51. Do not tweeze or wax your eyebrows off completely. They may not grow back.

1. Follow steps 1 thru 3 beginning on page 52 to draw the eyebrow for this style. The difference here compared to Wong's actual brows is that Wong's eyebrow more naturally followed her brow bone, and she did not completely remove the hair from her brow bone since her eyebrows were naturally high.

2. Apply a light brown shimmer eye shadow across the entire lid up to the eyebrow.

3. Using a small soft liner brush, apply a darker brown shimmer eye shadow in a sweep along the top lid and under the eye.

4. Apply a thin line of black eyeliner around the entire eye. Finish the eyes with a strip of false lashes and black mascara.

5. Apply a plum red blush to the cheeks. Wong's lips had a specific droop from the peak of the cupid's bow to the outer corner of the mouth that fell short of the outer corner. With this look, her bottom lip appeared to be slightly wider than the top creating a false smile. To enhance the shape after lipstick is applied, dab a small amount of gold powder makeup on the lower lip and the cupid's bow. (Refer to page 24 for tips on lipstick application.)

Greta Garbo Eyes

Many actresses in early Hollywood used makeup to develop their trademark look. Marlene Dietrich's eyebrows, Joan Crawford's lips and Greta Garbo's eyes were all created with makeup. Actress Greta Garbo had a distinct look to her eyes that was emphasized through her makeup. She enhanced her round eye shape by rounding her eyebrows to mimic the top of her eye and applying a heavy line in the crease of the upper eyelid to deepen the mood of her makeup.

The New Face

At the end of the 1930s, a new actress helped to usher in a new style of makeup that changed the idea of beauty in popular culture. Hedy Lamarr's full facial features, with the help of enhancement from Max Factor, proved to be influential and makeup into the next decade followed suit.[19]

1. Model Holly's natural eyebrow already has a high arch very similar to Lamarr. Her brow is darkened and the inner corner rounded with a dark brown eyebrow pencil.

2. Lamarr's eyebrows at the inner point were rounded and not very thick. To help create the illusion on these eyebrows, concealer is used to lighten the hairs below the brow that droop down too low.

3. Apply a wash of neutral shimmer eye shadow to make the lids appear even lighter and brighter and create contrast from the dark brows and lash line.

4. Apply a thin line of black eyeliner at the lash line, making it only slightly thicker on the outer half of the eye. Finish the eyes with a strip of false lashes and mascara.

5. Apply and blend in a light red blush. The lips are full and over-drawn on the top. The effect is the exact opposite of the look of Anna May Wong on the previous pages. Where as Wong's lower lip being longer created a false smile, Lamarr's upper lip being longer created the look of a false serious expression. (Refer to page 24 for tips on lipstick application.)

Makeup and T.V.

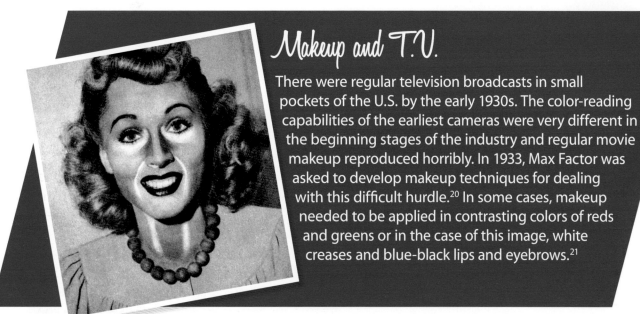

There were regular television broadcasts in small pockets of the U.S. by the early 1930s. The color-reading capabilities of the earliest cameras were very different in the beginning stages of the industry and regular movie makeup reproduced horribly. In 1933, Max Factor was asked to develop makeup techniques for dealing with this difficult hurdle.[20] In some cases, makeup needed to be applied in contrasting colors of reds and greens or in the case of this image, white creases and blue-black lips and eyebrows.[21]

The 1940s

The 1940s saw a more natural makeup application. The perception of makeup and what it represented shifted dramatically. Makeup was still very important, but heavy painting was taboo. There was a fine line between being too vain and letting yourself go. A woman was expected to pay attention to her appearance for the sake of those around her, the soldiers and her own personal pride, but if she overdid it, it was considered garish.

During the war, less makeup was applied. Rationing made it difficult to get some products and impossible to get others. Women came up with other options to replace the lack of makeup. Thanks to the pseudo pressure put on women to keep up their appearance during WWII, by 1948, it is estimated that 80 to 90 percent of American women used lipstick, two-thirds used rouge and a quarter used eye makeup.[1]

After the war ended, it took a couple years for manufacturers to catch up on production, but once things had returned to normal, a boom occurred in makeup. By the time 1950 rolled around, women had a multitude of new colors to choose from and styles to wear. Going without for so long led to a surplus.

News Release, 1939 [2]

"Twenty years ago Hollywood discovered the 'vampire.' The frizzy hair and the bandeau were regular vamp equipment, with a few spit curls filtering through. The cupid's bow mouth was heavily daubled with gooey lipstick, and the face was covered entirely with a greasepaint. Eyes were outlined with thick mascara. Today the screen's 'glamour girl,' as conceived by Max Factor, is a much neater article. A trend toward naturalness and technical improvements in photography and lighting cause her screen make-up to be almost the same as her street make-up."

In the mid-1940s, Evelyn Haynes wrote in *Vogue* that, "a new kind of beauty" had arrived. "The gentleness of the new beauty is reflected in make-up. Foundations will now be used with a feather touch. They will be used for their original purpose: to hold powder and not to drown the complexion."[3]

Eye shadow was rare, but for the daytime, a color that coordinated with eye color was best, and in the evening, shadow to coordinate with the dress was acceptable. Shadow colors were muted.[4] Application was light and blended only on the upper eyelid. For evening, "A drop of Herbal Tissue Oil on the lids before applying eye shadow," heightened glamour.[5]

Using a pencil to draw a fine line on the upper lash line was acceptable, but eyeliner's popularity had diminished since the 1930s due to its artificial appearance. "The lightest stroke can be used at the corners of the eyes to elongate the eyes."[6] Makeup on the lower lid was generally mascara only.

Women were still using cake mascara. If a woman did not use mascara, it was recommended that she at least brush her lashes with a brush moistened with Vaseline to remove powder and give the lashes and brows a sheen.[7] Some girls only applied mascara to the top lashes.

Lipstick was a staple and encouraged to help keep women's spirits up during the war. One application suggestion started at the outer corner of the upper lip and in to the center, then the top lip rolled to apply lipstick to the bottom lip. Then a lady's finger was to be used to blend the lipstick up into the cupid's bow.

Max Factor already had a lipstick pencil on the market and by 1948, Gala of London was also advertising their pencil *Lip Line*. In the late 1940s, Rimmel's lip pencils included the colors *Pink Purple*, *Pink Ice*, and *Dangerous Red*.[8]

Eyebrow and Lip Shapes

The shaved and redrawn eyebrows of the 1930s had all but disappeared. Some women still wore thin eyebrows, but the shift to a more natural look meant less tweezing. Tweezing involved removal of stray hair just to get a clean line. Reshaping was done only if you had very large, unruly eyebrows. "Be careful not to flatten the eyebrows on to the nose, but remove any hairs which grow across the bridge of the nose." *Good Housekeeping*, 1944.[9]

The taper also started to show up more in the 1940s, with the inner corner of the brow a little thicker and tapering up to the peak of the rounded arch to a point on the outer corner.

Neatly combing the brows with some oil, Vaseline or maybe a little mascara was used to deepen the color. Drawing eyebrows in with a pencil was left only to the very fair haired eyebrow or for some added glamour in the evening.[10]

The natural lip shape was the popular lip shape of the 1940s. Following the natural lines of the lips or slightly over-drawing if the upper lip was smaller than the bottom lip or vice versa.

In Hollywood, Joan Crawford's Hunter's Bow had heavily influenced the lips of the 1940s. The top lip on many actresses was broad and full, and the cupid's bow of the lip was overdrawn so that color went above the lip where it naturally drops off to taper to the outer corners of the mouth. Lana Turner used a heavy upper lip shape to offset her jawline.[11] A thin upper lip was rarely seen in Hollywood. The top and bottom lip were often painted to be equal size in relation to each other.

A few actresses who had natural lips that were equal in size on both top and bottom used their own natural lip shape. Actresses like Ingrid Bergman and Lauren Bacall left their thinner upper lip naturally shaped.

Coloring of the 1940s

Eye shadow was still available, but not used as often. Colors varied widely and rules usually still followed that a color should harmonize with the eyes during the day and in the evening something that went with the clothes could be used. Gold and silver were still popular evening colors, often to add gleam to other shadow colors.[12]

With lipstick, when we think of red today, it generally conjures up something on a country's flag, but descriptions of reds in cosmetic company rhetoric were very broad. They eluded more to "pastels of red."[13] To say something was rose red, meant it was rose. These were considered variations of what red could become with tone and color changes.

Elizabeth Arden offered *Colour Harmony Boxes* which included face powder, lipstick, rouge and eye shadow that were perfectly created to go together. The company suggested women choose color based on their costume instead of complexion.[14] Some of Arden's lipstick choices were *Radiant Peony* and *Cyclamen Day* on the pink side. *Victory Red*, *Stop Red*, *Burnt Sugar* and *Redwood* were heavily publicized as uniform appropriate during the war.

Revlon also created products to harmonize together, above and beyond the more well known lipstick and nail polish duos. The color *Ultra Violet*, described as "unearthly violet fired with rubies," included polish, lipstick, and a "mystic-mauve" face powder. Other color names in the Revlon line were *Plumb Beautiful* and *Bright Forecast*, a bright red.

Helena Rubenstein made it a little more complicated. The company did carry lipsticks and polish that went together, but powder was to be chosen by complexion, eye makeup based on eye color, and lipstick based on costume.[15]

Max Factor was selling red, red, and more red. The makeup line centered more around its face makeup and the lipstick line offered *Clear Red Numbers 1, 2* and *3*. *Blue Red* and *Rose Red* were also offered in three numbers, which were tonal changes from light to dark.

Other wartime colors were Tussy's *Jeep Red*, *Fighting Red* and *Safari* and Dorothy Grey sold *Crimson Glory* and *Headline Red*. Nail polish names would follow suit with the name of the lipstick created to match it.

Chen Yu nail polishes had names like *China Doll*, *Burma Red* and *Green Dragon*.

Seasons were another factor in determining color. In 1948, *The Queen* recommended strong lipstick in autumn like dark grape red, Arden's *Red Cactus*, or Yardley's *Copper Red*. In 1949, *Vogue* was predicting summer colors would be orange-red lipstick, coral rouge, beige powder, pale green eye shadow, and dark green or brown mascara with brown eyebrow pencil.[16]

On the more bizarre side, in 1941, *Vogue* advised, "Dramatize a good mouth. Put blue-red on the upper lip, orange-red on the lower."[17]

Toward the end of the decade colors softened from the deep reds, although it was still a staple for women to have. Pinks, corals and mauve were becoming more popular lip choices. Gala sold *Ballet Pink* and Pomeroy had *Almond Blossom*.

Nail Polish

WWII and... Makeup at Work

A lot of attention was paid to makeup during WWII. One might expect that it would be seen as frivolous to care about such things during such a serious time in history, but on the contrary, it was believed to be even more important.

The amount of makeup women wore had diminished because of rationing and the view that overdoing it was superficial and inappropriate, but makeup was still important for things such as attracting a man. The importance of down playing makeup so as not to be too garish changed the sales techniques though. "Invariably men appreciate the sensitive understatement of Elizabeth Arden lipstick shades which make them aware of the woman...not the make-up." Elizabeth Arden ad, circa 1940.

It was a part of a woman's duty during the war to keep herself attractive and well put together. *Technique for Beauty*, produced in the UK in 1940, told women, "The stress and strain of war can easily make you lose interest in your personal appearance, but it is up to you to take care of yourself for the sake of other people." Tangee ads during WWII used copy like, "A woman's lipstick is an instrument of personal morale that helps her to conceal heartbreak or sorrow; gives her self-confidence when it's badly needed; heightens her loveliness when she wants to look her loveliest."[18]

An advertisement for Barbara Gould cosmetics in 1943 reminded women that, "America expects its women to keep busy... and keep beautiful. Let Barbara Gould *Vibrant* colors in make-up help you look your loveliest for your new way of life." This new way of life included all the things that a good American woman could do to contribute to the war effort, like factory work or providing childcare for another working woman.

Keeping femininity through cosmetics during the demands of positions normally held by men was considered important to morale, productivity, and battling fatigue. Even the players of the All-American Girls Professional Baseball League, which provided the entertainment of America's past-time while male ballplayers were away at war, were required to take makeup lessons from Helena Rubenstein. Tangee ads praised women for "keeping your femininity - even though you are doing man's work."[19]

Some tips for these war workers included using products like Pond's Cold Cream or Max Factor's Normalizing Cream and lip pomades to protect them from becoming too red and rough if their job brought them outdoors through harsh weather conditions, such as at a ship yard. Rouge was acceptable if it was nearly undetectable. Otherwise it was too much.[20]

Some of the recommendations for nail care included weekly manicures at either the salon or at home and regular use of cuticle oils and hand creams. Olive oil was a good substitute for moisturizing.[21] A nurse may have been in danger of septic nails because of the constant hand scrubbing and exposure to infections. She was advised to take good care of her cuticles to avoid this.[22]

The length of a woman's nails was also an important sign as to whether or not she was doing her part. A war worker kept her nails shorter for safety reasons.[23]

The caption for this image created for the OEM reads, "Feminine vanity still demands attention - even in the nation's busy aircraft factories. At Cessna Aircraft Company's plant in Wichita, Kansas, Miss Weber takes a quick time out for facial repair, using a gleaming sheet of aluminum in the stock room as a mirror."

WWII and... Makeup During Rationing

Rationing hit the cosmetic industry hard. Supplies and ingredients became increasingly difficult to find, but also provided them with avenues for new products to counteract rationing of other goods.

Some items that were rationed that proved a challenge for companies included glass bottles. Although lipstick was considered indispensable to the war effort and morale, metal rationing affected Revlon, who had to change to a plastic container and later paper for their lipsticks. They also had trouble producing lipstick itself as the important ingredient castor oil had also been rationed.[24]

Max Factor's lipstick brush did well during this time thanks to tips like this one from *Woman's Weekly* in 1944. "Isn't it just too heartbreaking when your favorite, irreplaceable lipstick is reduced to the very end? Did you know that you can use the very end in the container if you paint it on with a camel hair brush?" If a lady ran out of lipstick and her local store was out of stock, beetroot juice stained the lips well and a Vaseline cover added shine.[25]

When mascara was scarce, women could go back to the home remedies used prior to commercial mascara's introduction. These included burnt cork, mustache wax, shoe polish or lamp black. Vaseline or brilliantine, a hair oil, added depth and shine to lashes and eyebrow hair.

Nail polish could be substituted with varnish, paint, or dope, a lacquer formerly used to waterproof cloth surfaces of airplane wings. A woman could also turn to stains such as beetroot or just buffing the nail for shine.

When nail polish had become completely banned, Cutex sold powder polish, a product that used a buffer to apply to the surface of the nail.[26]

Stockings became almost impossible to find due to silk, rayon and nylon, the most popular stocking materials, being almost completely reserved for military needs such as parachutes, tents, rope and tires. If word caught on that a shop might have some in stock, a line quickly formed out the door.

Makeup manufacturers solved this issue with leg makeup. Elizabeth Arden introduced *Velva Leg Film*, which claimed to be water resistant. Cyclax of London produced *Stockingless* and Helena Rubenstein introduced *Aquacade Leg Lotion*. Max Factor also produced a leg makeup cream. Most accounts of the time though claimed that if it started raining, the makeup would run.

How slim... How lovely your legs will look clad in this beautiful Velva Leg Film soft... smooth... water-resistant ... it lasts until washed away.

Elizabeth Arden

The biggest challenge to using this liquid was not the liquid itself. A friend with a steady hand needed to be found to draw the seam of the stocking with an eyebrow pencil up the back of the leg. Unlike modern day hose, stockings of the time had a seam in the back where it was sown together. Covering the leg with makeup was not just about making the skin look darker. Stockings were an extremely important part of dressing up, as important as the dress itself. Without that seam, a lady's outfit was not complete.[27]

WWII and... Makeup in the Military

Makeup with uniform was a touchy subject. Women in the service were not immune to the ideal that makeup was important for morale, but strict guidelines were to be followed to keep it appropriate.

"Do remember that obvious make-up looks out of place with the uniform," warned Jane Gordon in the 1940 beauty manual, *Technique for Beauty*. "Scarlet lipstick does not look so bad with navy blue and red piped A.F.S. uniform but it does look silly with khaki. The only lipsticks which look well with khaki are the natural pinks such as Tangee." For other uniforms, rose lipstick and rouge were appropriate.[28]

She also wrote, "Eye shadow is taboo with uniform, or should be." Gordon's thoughts on nails were, "National service work and elegantly long finger-nails do not go together, and of course nail varnish with uniform looks utterly ridiculous." She goes on to write that, "You will, however, find one of the varnish bases a godsend in keeping your nails from cracking and becoming rigid."

Cosmetic companies did not want to lose out because their products were inappropriate for service women. Cyclax of London provided a number of products geared directly to these women. In England, the 'Wrens' (Women's Royal Navy Service), were given a standard-issue *Auxiliary Red* lipstick formulated to go with their uniform. Cyclax of London also produced a *"Service" Beauty Kit* complete with essential makeup

Auxiliary Red

the lipstick for Service Women

The "trifle" that spells PERFECTION for your "Auxiliary" ensemble . . . dashing, decisive, enduring, supremely correct.

Tens of thousands of "Auxiliaries" will thank "Cyclax" for this newest of new Lipsticks . . . . . . it ends their quest . . . answers their "where?" "what?" "how?" . . . meets exactly their newly regimented need. Came the swift call . . . "Auxiliary Red" brought the swift, perfect, incomparable response.

"Service" Beauty Kit is a very compact and attractive morocco case in various colours (6½" by 4½" to fit uniform pocket) lined oil silk, fitted complete with essential make-up requisites. **22 6**

58 SOUTH MOLTON STREET, LONDC

Cyclax
OF LONDON

Cyclax "Service" Beauty Kit

requisites contained in a case designed to fit snuggly in a uniform pocket.[29]

Elizabeth Arden introduced *Montezuma Red* lipstick and nail polish developed to match the red chevrons and hat tassel of a female U.S. Marine officer uniform. According to rules, women's lipstick and nail lacquer had to match their uniform red perfectly in order to wear it.[30] In the U.S., an advertisement for an Elizabeth Arden lipstick reads, "And women love the subtle, carefully thought out Elizabeth Arden harmony between costume colors and lipstick shades...The young woman wears a Burnt Sugar Lipstick — most effective with khaki...many of her friends complement their uniforms of blue with the youthful vigor of Redwood." Women could buy another service kit from Elizabeth Arden. The kit had a pigskin case and contained Cleansing and Velva cream, foundation cream, lipstick, comb, mirror, and space for powder.

Helena Rubenstein's contribution came in the form of *Regimental Red*. The makeup range included lipstick, cream and compact rouge, and nail groom.[31]

Also in *Technique for Beauty*, Jane Gordon wrote, "Helena Rubenstein has also brought out a brand-new lipstick especially made for black-out conditions. This is a very dark luminous lipstick which includes special ingredients to make the lips glow. "[32] The element added to this glow-in-the-dark makeup to create this effect was undoubtedly radium, used for luminous paints at the time and the same radioactive material that its discoverer Madame Curie died from exposure to.

Women in uniform who carry respirators were warned, "No woman with a respirator should wear an ordinary eyelash cosmetic for the simple reason that after the respirator has been worn for a few minutes the moisture produced by the breath will make the eyelash cosmetic run and it will probably run into the eyes." Their options to counter this issue were eyelash dyeing, which carried risks, or a waterproof eyelash cosmetic made by Leichner.[33]

The U.S. Marine Corps commissioned Max Factor in 1943 to create a special makeup used to camouflage the faces of soldiers against backdrops such as sand, barren earth, jungle foliage and night.[34]

Mame

Rita Hayworth and actresses like her influenced the minimal makeup look of the 1940s. A natural beauty who required few changes in appearance, her sparkling eyes balanced by her slightly overdrawn lips made her what many consider to be one the most beautiful film actresses of all time.

1. To make eyebrows appear thinner, use your thumb placed above the eyebrow and an eyebrow wand below the eyebrow and press the hair in between them with light pressure toward the center of the line of the eyebrow. A brow gel color developed for redheads is used here to bring the eyebrow hair color closer to the natural hair color.

2. Use a sharp eyebrow pencil to elongate the eyebrow out past the eye in a fine line.

3. Using a small eye shadow brush, apply a warm eye shadow on the lower part of the upper eyelid and blend.

4. Apply a very fine line of liquid eyeliner at the base of the lashes only on the upper eyelid to thicken the appearance of the lashes. Finish the eyes with a layer of mascara. False lashes can be used if the natural lashes are very fine. In this case use an eyelash glue that dries clear to keep the upper lid from appearing too heavy and made up.

5. Apply warm bronzer below the cheek bone to contour the face. The lipstick color is a warm brick red. Model Kira's lips are altered quite a bit for this look. Because her natural cupid's bow peak is higher, the peaks are covered with foundation and the lipstick placed lower on the lip. Then to make the area of her upper lip outside of the cupid's bow appear more full and even with the size of her lower lip, the lips are over-drawn. The drop from the peak of the cupid's bow to the outer corner of the mouth is soft and even. (Refer to page 24 for tips on lipstick application.)

Jazz Singer

More often heard on the radio than seen on the silver screen, Billie Holiday's strong features and expressive face added to her beauty and performance on stage. Her full lips and eyebrows were important to defining her face on stage under the spotlights, where makeup must be heavy to show up.

1. The eyebrows for this makeup are thick and dark. Add a dark brown eyebrow shadow with an angled eyebrow brush to deepen the color. Use an eyebrow pencil of similar color to thicken the eyebrows if necessary.

2. Use a highlight pencil or highlight eye shadow directly below the eyebrow to enhance the shape and dimension of the eyelid.

3. Apply a medium brown eye shadow with shimmer to the entire eyelid.

4. Apply a gold eye shadow down the middle of the eyelid to give the appearance of a wet eyelid and add glamour to the makeup.

5. Finish the eyes with a thin line of liquid eyeliner at the base of the lashes only on the upper eyelid, a strip of long false lashes glued down with dark-toned eyelash glue and a coat of mascara.

6. Apply a raspberry blush softly on the lower part of the apples of the cheeks. Because model Patricia's natural cupid's bow peaks are close together, the steps from page 24 are used to redraw this portion of her lip so that the rise from the middle of her lip up to the peaks is wider and rounder. Lip color is deep brick red and the lips are over-drawn slightly just outside of the cupid's bow to increase the fullness of the top lip.

Ilsa

In the 1940s, European actresses like Ingrid Bergman wore very little makeup both on screen and off. Her eyebrows were natural and untweezed and her lipstick choice often appeared as if it could be her natural lip color. The inspiration behind this makeup was to take a model who appears to have natural contrast in her features and make her as natural as possible, almost appearing to have on no makeup, but also keep the look 1940s appropriate.

1. Model Devon's naturally dark eyebrows are brushed with an eyebrow gel made for blondes to lighten the hair and make the eyebrow appear less "done."

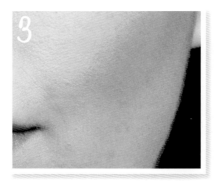

2. The same blonde eyebrow gel is brushed on her dark eyelashes to lighten them. This still adds thickness to the lashes, but keeps them from appearing as if they have heavy mascara on them.

3. A warm bronzer is brushed onto the cheeks to give contour and a sun-kissed glow.

4. Pale coral lipstick is applied to follow the natural line of the lips to finish the look. If the lower lip is not already full, slightly over-draw it to give it extra pout.

Silk Beauty Patches

In the late 1940s, beauty patches had a short-lived comeback. Made of silk, they came in boxes of 100, cut into shapes of circles, triangles, squares, diamonds, hearts, stars, half-moons, arrows, cloverleafs and human figures.[35]

The 1950s

"With a clink of vials and a wafting of odors, the mysterious rite begins. It is 6:45 a.m., and her husband still abed, but pretty Mrs. James Locke sits before a mirrored table in her three-room San Francisco apartment, her blonde hair covered by a filmy nylon cap...She cleans her skin of night cream, anoints it with icy water — and for one brief moment shows her true face. Then, slowly, comes the metamorphosis.

"Over her face she spreads a foundation cream, creating a pale and expressionless mask. She caresses her cheeks with a liquid rouge, slowly adding color to her face, tops it off by gently patting on a flesh-colored powder. She shadows her eyes with turquoise, dabs a few drops... With a dark pencil she shapes her eyebrows to give an artificial lift to her expression, brushes her eyelashes with a pen like wand to emphasize her blue eyes...The final touch — an orange lipstick to match her fingernail polish."
Time magazine, 1958[1]

After the conservative years of WWII came to an end and the cosmetics industry caught back up with demand, makeup style took the biggest turn seen to date. Things were getting better for people financially and along with brightly colored kitchen appliances and couches came bright and shapely makeup. Fins on cars, chevrons on kitchen cabinet handles and well-defined eyebrows became the look of the day.

Kurlash

Much to the happiness of women everywhere, and their eyelashes, in the early 1950s, Kurlash improved its design by adding a cushion to their eyelash curler. Prior to this, the eyelash curler was all metal and very hard on lashes.[2] Companies quickly followed and by 1955, Maybelline advertised a woman could "Look prettier — through curly lashes in just seconds — with the new soft-cushion Maybelline Professional Eyelash Curler," available gold plated for $1.[3]

The Wing

The original doe-eye began toward the end of the 1940s and by the early '50s was one of the most popular styles of eyeliner. "We pencil the corner of the eye upward to make it almond-shaped." said Dr. Gould for Helena Rubenstein in 1950.[4] It is appropriate to line only the outer half of the eye for the doe-eye look.

By the mid-1950s the cat eyeliner reached across the top of the eyelid in any number of variations in length, thickness, flip, and color and was all over fashion magazines. The line was sometimes added to the bottom lid, but most often only mascara was added to the lower lid.

Elizabeth Arden sold a beauty kit complete with a small, thin brush for applying the cake eyeliner that came in the kit. Maybelline called their version Fluid Eye-liner.

This style of flip was a very important part of the decade's makeup look and has many options for soft and striking variations.

The various products for this look include pencil, liquid, marker (another form of liquid) and gel eyeliner. Another option not shown here is an eye shadow converter. Available from most professional makeup lines, it allows you to turn a favorite eye shadow color into a liner by liquefying the shadow for painting and hardening after it dries.

Pencil

A pencil may not create the crispest line, but it is blendable.

Liquid

A quality liquid looks nice, but careful not to choose one that flakes after it dries.

Marker

A marker liner is a thinner liquid applied through the sponge point.

Gel

A nice choice for a soft color and a hard line applied with a liner brush.

Liner with Staying Power

1. Getting lines and points even takes practice. For more even application, sharpen an eyeliner pencil to a point and stare directly into the mirror. Mark a dot in the spot where you want the wing point to end on the outer corner. Mark the other side and check that the dots are even.

2. Then from that point draw inward toward the eye using more of the side of the eyeliner point to apply color.

3. You can leave the line at this point or use a long even stroke to fill in and draw the line across the top of the eye.

4. Finish by setting the line with a gel or liquid eyeliner to deepen the color and sharpen the edges.

Tips

A wing liner can be done on any eye shape. Creativity just needs to be used to get the effect. On either a monolid or hooded eyelid, the upper eyelash line often disappears under the lid. **1.** To get the look of the continuous line, lower where the point will be and continue the dark line under the eye. Wear extra mascara or add a small section of false lashes on the outer corner. **2** and **3.** Extra liner can be added on the top to get a line above the eye.

For close set or very round eyes, consider keeping the eyeliner only on the outer third of the eye. For eyes that droop on the outer corner, leave a few millimeters of skin colorless below the wing.

In the 1950s, eyeliner color for fair hair and skin was often brown. Deep plum is also a soft color for daytime.

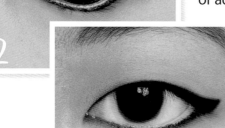

Variations

The possibilities for the wing eyeliner are endless. By changing the length, thickness, flip and color, the appearance of the eye and the rest of the makeup change dramatically.

All of the eyeliner options in this section are inspired by women in different advertisements and beauty books from the 1950s.

Eyeliner seen in 1954 beauty book.

Eyeliner seen in Dorothy Grey makeup advertisement.

Eyeliner seen in image of actress Mitzi Gaynor.

Eyeliner seen in 1957 *Vogue Beauty Book*.

Eyeliner worn by queen of the cat liner, Sophia Loren, in 1960.

Eyeshadow Style

By the mid-1950s, eyeshadow brightened to distinctive colors of blue, green and purple. The placement of these bold colors spanned the width of the eyelid from inner to outer point. Most women kept it subtle using a wash of color that covered the lower part of the upper eyelid. Women also applied it so that just a peek of the color appeared above their black wing eyeliner. (Refer to pages 79 and 92 for more views of these styles.)

Eyebrow and Lip Shapes

The eyebrows of the 1950s varied widely in shape and size. The general rule followed was that tweezing should happen below the eyebrow, not above, and all had in common an artificial painting in. It was customary to take whatever you had, tweeze it to a clean line and then use a pencil to darken in and possibly thicken.

Most eyebrows tapered from a thick inner corner out to a clean point. The inner corner was round or squared. The ascent to the peak could be a straight line to a pointed peak or a gradual rounded eyebrow was popular. A straight brow was also *en vogue*.

In the mid-1950s, the Mandarin eyebrow made its way to America from Paris. This eyebrow shape involved completely tweezing out the outer corner of the eyebrow and drawing it back in with an upward sweep.

Mandarin Brow

Lip shape in the 1950s for the regular girl followed the basic shape of the natural mouth. Since softer colors were becoming more popular, a softer mouth shape was desirable.

Other trends included a curvier top lip. In the 1940s, the rounded Hunter's Bow had an even fall from the peak to the outer corner. In the 1950s, Hollywood tapered the fall from the peak to the outer corner for a droop that almost mimicked a pleasant, innocent smile.

Sultry movie stars like Marilyn Monroe and Sylvia Lopez were over-drawing the top lip for a full look. This sometimes had an even fall from peak to outer corner and some women allowed the dip described earlier for a pleasant expression.

Coloring of the 1950s

Colors were wide and varied in the 1950s, but the decade started with the conservative ideas of the 1940s. Colorful eye shadow was coming into fashion, but did not catch on right away.

More conservative women still wore a lighter touch of eye shadow that coordinated with eye color. In the Fall of 1950, Hazel Rawson Cades advised women in *Woman's Home Companion* to "apply mascara only to upper lashes for the most natural effect," and warned that "eye shadow was meant to be shadow, not a colour accent, and should be used sparingly."[5]

As the decade wore on, color was more acceptable and women were wearing eye shadows the same color as the bright couches in their living rooms. Beauty magazines gave women full permission to play up on color choices now available. Fashion models were wearing heavy mascara and doe-eyed liner in various thicknesses, with bright shades of eye shadow accenting the lash line.

Revlon eye shadow colors included a *Mauve Frost, Fresh Violet, Blue Ice, Silver, Green Frost, Evergreen, Pistachio* and *Gold*. Mascara colors included *Fresh Violet, Blue Ice, Titian* and *Evergreen*. Eyeliner colors were *Evergreen, Walnut* and *Blue Frost*. Combinations could include the *Blue Frost* eyeliner with *Fresh Violet* mascara or *Evergreen* eye shadow with *Titian* mascara.[6]

In 1953, Aziza proposed women wear two colors of mascara, the darker one on the outer corner lashes.

In 1955, Lancome had 38 shades of lipstick "from the palest coral rose to the deepest exotic red" and 19 shades of cream eye shadow, six of which were iridescent.

In 1953, *The Queen* suggested an untanned blonde wear pink lipstick and rouge with pearly green eye shadow during the day and cherry lipstick and rouge with theatrical green eye shadow at night.[7] Brown eyeliner/eyebrow pencil was suggested for blondes and red-heads. Black eyeliner/eyebrow pencil was acceptable for brunettes and brownettes.

In 1958, *Vogue* liked grey eye shadow, grey eyebrow/eyeliner pencil and smoky mascara with bright lipstick like true-red, orange or pink-orange.[8]

Red lipstick was still very popular, but pinks and corals were everywhere too. A woman was to have a lipstick for each season and for day and evening. Lipstick and nail polish still matched in the 1950s.

Rouge was still used, but had become almost unseen. Emphasis was on the eyes and the lips. The rosy cheek began to faze out in the 1940s and by the '50s blusher was more for contour than adding color to the cheeks.

Many eye shadows came in cream, stick or liquid form.

The Showgirl

Of all the influential faces of the 1950s, Marilyn Monroe could not be summed up in just one makeup style. Featured here are two makeup looks inspired by her. First is a very natural makeup reminiscent of not only her, but other blonde actresses like Kim Novak and Janet Leigh.

1. The high pointed eyebrow is created by first brushing the inner half of the eyebrow up and to the right with a wand with eyebrow gel, even forcing some of the hair at the peak to point out above the eyebrow. Then the outer part of the eyebrow is combed down and to the right.

2. Fill in the peak of the eyebrow with an eyebrow pencil.

3. Apply a soft, very light pink eye shadow across the entire upper eyelid.

4. Use a dark brown eyeliner pencil to draw a fine line at the base of the lashes of the upper eyelid and create a small wing line that comes just out of the outer corner of the eye. Do not add liner on the lower eyelid. Finish the eyes with dark brown mascara.

5. A pale pink blush is added to the lower part of the apples of the cheeks and blended back to the ears. The upper lip is over-drawn outside the natural lip line to create a wider cupid's bow and fuller top lip. Add a brown beauty mark to keep the look soft. (Refer to page 50 for more information on creating a beauty mark.)

Velvety Lashes

To keep in line with her company's appearance of luxury, Elizabeth Arden suggested the style of velvety eyelashes. Use a razor blade to scrape a black velvet ribbon and then dip a wand wet with mascara into the pile of black fluff to apply to the lashes.[9]

The Bombshell

The most mimicked look of Marilyn Monroe is her "movie star" image, complete with sultry red lips and thick eyeliner. These steps are for a more natural look that are not meant to make the face look like the person, just capture the essence of her glowing skin and bedroom eyes.

1. The high pointed eyebrow is created by first brushing the inner half of the eyebrow up and to the right with a wand with eyebrow gel, even forcing some of the hair at the peak to point out above the eyebrow. Then the outer part of the eyebrow is combed down and to the right.

2. Fill in the peak of the eyebrow with an eyebrow pencil.

3. Apply a light, neutral eye shadow to the entire eyelid. Then apply a rose colored shimmer eye shadow to the upper eyelid,

being sure to concentrate the color in the area of the crease of the eyelid.

4. Using a black pencil eyeliner, draw a soft line that begins at the inner corner of the eye and runs along the lash line of the upper eyelid to the outer corner. Draw a small wing out that begins just above the outer corner of the eye. This naturally gives a rise to the appearance of the eye. If the wing is too low, it makes the eye appear to droop. Then, with a flat eyeliner brush and liquid eyeliner, add darkness directly at the lash line of the upper eyelid. Pull this line slightly past the inner corner of the eye to elongate.

5. Add three or four single eyelash clusters to the outer corner of the eye to increase the doe-eyed effect. Finish the eye makeup with black mascara.

6. Use a warm bronzer below the cheek and on the lower part of the apple of the cheek to add contour and the appearance of sun exposure.

7. Use a warm shimmer cream to add highlight on the temples and the upper part of the cheekbone. Monroe's makeup often had a glimmer to it that gave her a healthy sun-kissed glow.

8. Lips are over-drawn to give the appearance of fullness and equal thickness between the top and bottom lip. Like the makeup on the previous pages, the upper lip is given a full round cupid's bow. (Refer to page 24 for tips on lipstick application.) Finish the look with a soft black beauty mark. (Refer to page 50 for more information on creating a beauty mark.)

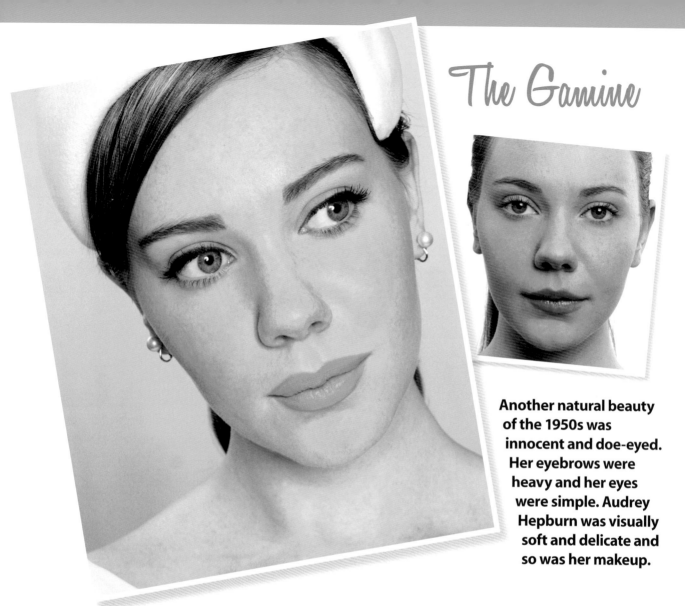

Another natural beauty of the 1950s was innocent and doe-eyed. Her eyebrows were heavy and her eyes were simple. Audrey Hepburn was visually soft and delicate and so was her makeup.

1. The 1950s saw a great change in eyebrow shape. Fine eyebrows became medium thickness and medium eyebrows grew heavy and thick. Heavy brows with soft makeup do not look as harsh. When over-drawing eyebrows it is easier to control shape using a sharp eyebrow pencil. It may seem jarring at first, but use a clean eyebrow wand to lightly brush the applied makeup and soften the lines. The inner corner of the eyebrow is squared off, which was very specific to the 1950s. Prior to this decade, the inner corner of the eyebrow was generally rounded.

2. Apply a pale pink eye shadow to the entire upper eyelid.

3. Apply a medium brown eye shadow with a hint of lavender in it to the upper eyelid beginning near the lash line and blending up to the eyebrow.

4. With a chocolate brown eyeliner pencil, draw a fine line that begins at the inner corner of the eye and runs along the lash line of the upper eyelid. As the line works its way to the outer corner, it should get slightly thicker and end in a small wing point.

5. Curl the eyelashes and apply black mascara. Cut about one-third of the outer part of a strip of false lashes off and apply mascara to them abundantly. After the mascara has dried, apply them using a clear eyelash glue. These steps are a little different from previous makeups that placed dark color at the base of the lashes to increase the appearance of the thickness of the lashes. The reason is to increase the apparent thickness of the actual eyelash hairs without making the top eyelid feel heavy and weighed down.

6. Apply a bright pale pink blush to the lower part of the apples of the cheeks and blend out to the ears. The upper lip is over-drawn outside of the cupid's bow to increase the thickness of the lip. This makes it appear slightly longer than the lip below it to keep in fashion with the style of Hepburn's makeup, whose lower lip appeared shorter. (Refer to page 24 for tips on lipstick application.)

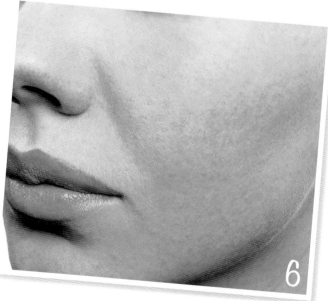

The Supermodel

Model Suzy Parker had a diverse face, which helped her become one of the most famed models of the 1950s, landing numerous *Vogue* covers and ads for Revlon. The steps below are inspired by a simple headshot in which her features are well defined with strong lips and a natural wing eyeliner.

1. Use a sharp eyebrow pencil to draw in the eyebrow. The inner corner of the eyebrow is squared off. Fill in a high pointed peak above the eyebrow that quickly descends into a sharp point at the outer corner of the eyebrow.

2. Apply a warm, rose brown shimmer eye shadow to the upper eyelid near the lash line and blend up into the crease.

3. For a softer look, a chocolate brown eyeliner was used here, but this can also be done with black. Picture two imaginary lines that run from

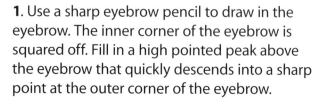

the eyebrow and the wing of the eyeliner and try to draw the wing of the eyeliner so that these two lines would connect close to the eye. It is easier to achieve this look by starting the point of the wing first.

4. Finish and fill in a thin line of the eyeliner across the entire eye.

5. Finish the eyes with black mascara.

6. Apply a warm blush to contour the cheeks and a warm brick red lipstick.

Revlon

Revlon's first advertisement was in *The New Yorker* in 1935.[10] The company soon developed an advertising strategy that set them apart from all of their competitors. Their tradition of color campaigns inviting women to become the woman of the ad was so popular that women were naming their bowling teams after the color lines like the "Fatal Apples" and the "Pink Lightnings."[11] When the campaign for *Fire and Ice* lipstick and nail polish featuring model Dorian Leigh in a silver sequin dress hit newsstands in 1952, many considered it to be "one of the most effective ads in cosmetic's history."[12] Revlon's fresh approach to appealing to a woman's sense of individuality made it a popular brand to the youth of the 1950s, who did not want to wear their mother's makeup.[13]

The 1960s

The greatest changes in cosmetic style of the 20th century came about in the 1960s and still greatly influences how makeup artists work today. Since the early 1900s, makeup was concentrated on certain parts of the face and color was expected to be brighter in some areas rather than others. This face of heavy lips, colorful cheeks and lash line shadow took a 180 degree turn during the 1960s.

The decade's makeup style began as a continuation of the 1950s, but, by the middle of the decade, flamboyant youth were playing with makeup style, standing out with bright colors and dark lines like the models of fashion magazines. Makeup was obvious and attention grabbing. Girls were not worried about the status quo or blending in to the group, much like the flapper of the 1920s.

Influences shifted away from movie stars and onto models and rock stars. The new supermodels were Twiggy, Peggy Moffit and Jean Shrimpton. These new fashion icons were creative, fun and influencing pop culture.

Color television and better magazine printing provided full color views of makeup to follow and more opportunities for cosmetic companies to highlight their wide array of color options.

Colored Beauty Mark

In 1961, *Mademoiselle* magazine suggested a colored beauty mark. The color was preferably blue and was created by applying two different colored eyeliner pencil colors, one on top of the other. Blue and turquoise were a good combination.[1] (Refer to page 50 for more information on creating a beauty mark.)

Although there were many developments in makeup at the time, the defining difference of the 1960s was the change in eye makeup. Fashion magazines and makeup artists like Pablo Manzoni, former creative director of Elizabeth Arden, had great influence over this change.

In previous decades, the color and dark liner were concentrated at the lash line and just above it. The new makeup of the day added darkness in the crease, kept a clean space between it and the darkened lash line, and introduced contouring to the masses. In the 1950s, the use of brown eye shadow near the crease was making its way into magazines, but by the '60s eye shadow had permanently moved into the crease, keeping the lower part of the upper eyelid prominent.

Often, dark lines with little to no blending were drawn into the crease. These lines were generally not connected to the makeup of the lash line. Makeup brushes were more common, making this precise makeup application much easier.[2]

The wing eyeliner was making its way out. It still popped up during the early part of the 1960s, but by the middle of the decade young girls applied their dark liners across the lid with added thickness in the center. The outer corners of liner still could come to a point, but instead of flipping the wing up, it went straight out or even down to make the eye look rounded and innocent.

In 1964, "big, beautiful, battable, believable" eyelashes were *Mademoiselle*'s suggestion. Extravagant lashes were everywhere.[3]

Eyebrows were still drawn in by some, but the youth of the 1960s kept their eyebrows natural, putting their energies more into eyeliner and shadow. Eyebrows were also rounded out more.[4]

Lips were de-emphasized with lighter pastel colors and a lighter application. Shape followed the natural curve of the lip. The cupid's bow was not defined and its edges blended into the natural skin

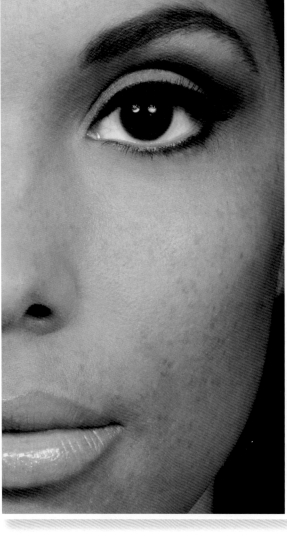

around the mouth.[5]

Prior to the 1960s, the makeup norm was clean, beautiful skin achieved through foundation and powder and lips smeared with lipstick. By 1960, foundation was considered heavy and dirty, so Covergirl marketed their product as "clean makeup...so natural you can't believe it's makeup."[6]

A common makeup style in fashion magazines, this eye makeup allows for many variations. Try it with a charcoal pencil in the crease and blend the edges of the line for a softer look.

1960s Eyes

The young models of the mid-1960s greatly influenced everyone. Their creative makeup styles were just as important to trends as the makeup artists of the day. The most famous models had their own signature makeup styles.

Twiggy's famous painted-on lower lashes were an original idea inspired by a babydoll she owned.[7] Yardley introduced false Twiggy Lashes for use at home.

Peggy Moffitt, inspired by the makeup worn by Kabuki performers, made her face and lips pale and drew elaborate, colorful lines around her eyes in combinations of black, white, pinks and orange. Cathy Dahmen used fine natural hairs to create delicate, long lashes on her lower eyelid as opposed to the thick black lines of Twiggy.

To the left, this common makeup style was seen on models like Jean Shrimpton in fashion magazines.
1. Apply eye shadow color of choice in a light layer over the entire lid. Blue was a popular color of the time, along with green and light neutrals.
2. Use a liquid liner to draw a thin line in the crease and along the lash line. Do not connect the lines.
3. Add false lashes using a dark-toned glue.

Crease line with dot, circa 1965

Twiggy babydoll eyelashes

Wide-eyed makeup, circa 1966

Peggy Moffitt Kabuki style makeup

Coloring of the 1960s

Although makeup was heavier in application, eyeliner color was less intense, with many women wearing brown and grey eyeliner rather than black. The wing of the eyeliner was also not flipped up as much as it had been in the 1950s. It now went straight out in the direction of the natural point of the eye.

Eye shadow in a number of brown tones made the heavy eye shadow look less garish and more about contour and shading. Blue, green, turquoise and silver were popular eye shadow colors, sometimes added as an accent at the lashes or put on as a light color wash along the entire lid.

Eye shadow was starting to migrate up the eyelid. In 1961, *Vogue* suggested, "liquid white foundation around the eyes, then with coloured grease shadow, draw a line just at the eyelid crease, smooth and blend it slightly upward — leaving the actual lid and bone area near the brow uncoloured by anything but the white foundation. The grease shadow could be set with a matching shade of powdered shadow, liquid eyeliner applied in a fairly narrow line," at the lash line.[8]

Pale pink lips were the most popular choice. The pink varied from light magenta to ballet pinks. Another option for toned down lip color was variations in brown lipstick including tans, sand, and cinnamon.

Warm, light coral, amber, apricot, sunbronze and pale tangerine were popular warm color options. Green eye shadow with these warm lipsticks was sometimes worn.

Revlon lip colors included *Bare Beige, Swinging Pink, Blase Apricot* and *Madly Mauve*. Coty lip color names included *Pure Apricot, Pure Honey, Pure Mango, Pure Cherry, Pure Cranberry, Pure Strawberry, Pure Pumpkin, Pure Watermelon, Pure Orchid* and *Pure Peppermint*. This went along well with *Vogue*'s 1962 prediction that the trend in lipstick was "toward clear, bright, outspoken colours. The reds are true reds, the pinks are practically essence-of-pink."

That same year, the Golden Look for summer was "golden tan or beige foundation, coral, amber or orange lipstick, charcoal or brown eyebrow pencil, brown, black or blue mascara, and blue, blue-green, or blue-violet eye shadow."[9]

Most often, when a makeup description during the early and mid-20th century mentions a certain color of eyebrow pencil, it is referring to the color of pencil to be used on the eyes also. Most pencils were double duty. An eyebrow pencil also acted as the eyeliner.

Mascara choices were black, brown-black, blue-black, green-black, grey-black, and golden-black.[10]

Nail polish colors were pale such as nude, pink, tan, ivory and pearl. Matching nails and lips was not as emphasized. Coordinating everything together was replaced with a mixture of warm and cool tones. Makeup companies still produced lipstick and nail polish coordinates, but less pressure was put on women to wear them together. More advertisements showed women with mismatched colors.

Eye Shadows

This makeup is inspired by a combination of a specific makeup from *Vogue* in 1963 and the common makeup style of the late 1950s and early '60s. This common style in fashion magazines combined a deep pencil eye shadow color, often in blue, with a thin, dark line and wing on the lash line.

1. Use an eyebrow pencil to lightly define the shape of the eyebrow. This eyebrow comes to high point at the peak and descends to a sharp point at the outer corner.

2. Apply a bright green eye shadow thickly along the lower part of the upper eyelid bringing it out into a soft wing.

3. Use a larger eye shadow brush to apply a soft brown above the green and blend the top edge of the green eye shadow.

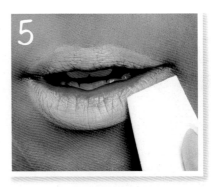

4. Using a very fine-pointed angled liner brush and a gel or liquid black eyeliner, draw a fine line along the lash line of the upper eyelid. Picture two imaginary lines that run from the eyebrow and the wing of the eyeliner and try to draw the wing of the eyeliner so that these two lines would connect close to the eye. Open the eye and apply a fine line of eyeliner along the lower lash line. Finish the eyes with black mascara. The original inspiration for this makeup did not have heavy, false lashes, but a natural-looking false eyelash strip applied with dark-toned eyelash glue can be used.

5. For a makeup in which the lips need to be redrawn into a different shape, a foundation and powder the same color as the skin tone should be used. In this makeup, the purpose of adding foundation to the lips is instead meant to even and lighten the underlying lip color so that the lipstick will appear lighter and more vibrant.

6. Apply a tangerine orange blush and lipstick that follows the natural lines of the lips.

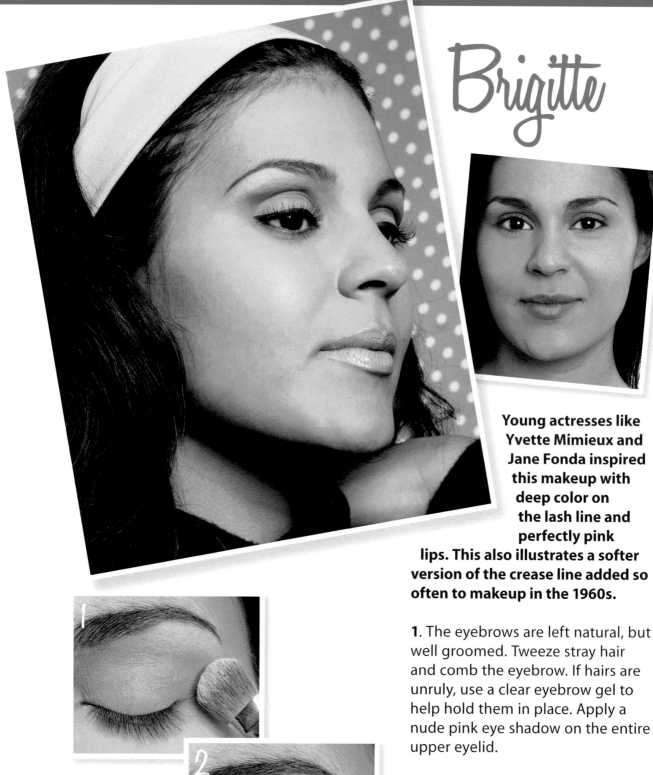

Brigitte

**Young actresses like
Yvette Mimieux and
Jane Fonda inspired
this makeup with
deep color on
the lash line and
perfectly pink
lips. This also illustrates a softer
version of the crease line added so
often to makeup in the 1960s.**

1. The eyebrows are left natural, but
well groomed. Tweeze stray hair
and comb the eyebrow. If hairs are
unruly, use a clear eyebrow gel to
help hold them in place. Apply a
nude pink eye shadow on the entire
upper eyelid.

2. With a soft liner brush apply a rose
brown eye shadow directly into the
crease of the upper eyelid and blend it
softly. Do not blend it so that the color
reaches the lash line.

3. With an angled eyeliner brush and a black gel or liquid eyeliner, apply a fine line along the lash line of the upper eyelid and drag it so it only slightly reaches outside of the outer corner of the eye into a short wing. Be careful not to draw the wing so that it flips up. The wing should only come straight out from the corner of the eye. Finish the eyes with black mascara and, if desired, a strip of false lashes applied with a dark-toned eyelash glue.

4. Apply a soft pink blush on the lower part of the apple of the cheeks back to the ears. Then apply a shimmer highlight lightly to the top of the apple of the cheek. Apply a nude pink lipstick.

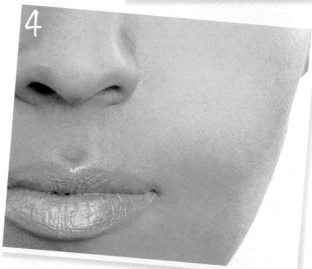

Lashes of the '60s

Thick false lashes were all the rage in the 1960s. Makeup artists would pile three strips on top of each other. **1**. The best way to do this is to apply one strip first. Allow the glue to dry. **2**. Place the second strip on the first as close to the skin as possible without touching the skin. **3**. As the lashes are placed, each consecutive strip will not reach as long across the eye as the strip before, so place it toward the outer corner. The effect will be a fanned out look. Another false lash technique of the 1960s used two-toned eyelashes. Using these steps, apply two different colors of eyelash strips. A makeup artist might have used green and brown, blue and black, brown and black, green and blue, or henna and brown.

Cleopatra Craze

When *Cleopatra* was released in 1963, a beauty craze was unleashed onto the entire world. Fashion magazines, hairstylists and cosmetic companies quickly jumped on this fad. Although it was not heavily worn by the public, it gave people in the beauty industry a fun style to work with.

This Egyptian Look followed the liquid liner of the 1950s and early '60s easily and was a helpful transition to the heavily lined makeup of the mid-1960s. *Look* magazine reported that this makeup style meant boldly-painted lips with the lower lip fuller than the top, eyes lined heavy with black and eye shadow in Nile green or white highlight, and eyebrows pencilled in black.[11]

Magazines provided their own versions of the eye makeup based on the movie. Wig makers and hairstylists created fashionable bobs and bouffants to mimic Elizabeth Taylor's movie hairstyles.

Revlon and the "Sphinx Eye"

Revlon created a line of makeup to coincide with the release of *Cleopatra* and put famed and favorite Revlon model Suzy Parker in one of their two-page spreads touting, "if looks can kill...this one will!" The unique Sphinx Doll case for the *Sphinx Pink* lipstick included a tiny bust of the queen attached to the cap

This "new idea in eye makeup" combined the cake liner lines and colored-in exotic eyebrows popular since the 1950s and the new Cleopatra craze sweeping the U.S. and Europe.

The eye makeup set came with complete instructions for applying "an enchanting new kind of sorcery — 2,000 years old!" The eye set included *Desert Beige* and *Misty Grey* eye shadows and *Black* or *Brown Ash* cake eyeliner and brushes.

1. Although not part of the original steps of the Revlon look, apply foundation to the eyelid and nude powder to set.

2. With a small, slightly moistened brush, apply a light beige eye shadow. It should be a few shades lighter than your natural skin tone.

3. Apply a thin line of cake or gel liner under the eye beginning at the middle of the eye and extending one-third inch out straight. This line should not flip up.

4. Apply the liner on the upper lash beginning at the inner corner of the eye and out to the outer corner connecting to the line on the lower part of the eye.

5. For this look, draw the section of the eyebrow closest to the nose thickly to the peak. The section to the outside of the peak thins and dips slightly much like the Mandarin style brow of the 1950s.

6. Last, apply a light coat of medium grey eye shadow on the upper lid above where the beige shadow was applied, avoiding overlapping.

Notes

For full citations please consult the bibliography.

A Little Her-story

1. Recounted in Richard Corson, *Fashions in Makeup*, p. 442.
2. Teresa Riordan, *Inventing Beauty*, p. 2.
3. Teresa Riordan, *Inventing Beauty*, p. 5.
4. Kathy Peiss, *Hope in a Jar*, p. 19.
5. Teresa Riordan, *Inventing Beauty*, p. 5.
6. Richard Corson, *Fashions in Makeup*, p. 435.
7. James Bennett, cosmeticsandskin.com, "Queen Alexandra and Face Enamelling."
8. Teresa Riordan, *Inventing Beauty*, p. 4.
9. Teresa Riordan, *Inventing Beauty*, p. 7.
10. *The Powder and the Glory*, DVD.

To Start

1. Teresa Riordan, *Inventing Beauty*, p. 9.
2. James Bennett, cosmeticsandskin.com, "1910 Cosmetic Timeline."
3. Kathy Peiss, *Hope in a Jar*, p. 15.
4. Teresa Riordan, *Inventing Beauty*, p. 16.
5. Kathy Peiss, *Hope in a Jar*, p. 58.
6. Teresa Riordan, *Inventing Beauty*, p. 7.
7. James Bennett, cosmeticsandskin.com, "Maybelline."
8. Richard Corson, *Fashions in Makeup*, p. 442.
9. James Bennett, cosmeticsandskin.com, "1910 Cosmetic Timeline."
10. Teresa Riordan, *Inventing Beauty*, p. 37.
11. James Bennett, cosmeticsandskin.com, "1920 Cosmetic Timeline."
12. Jane Gordon, *Technique for Beauty*, p. 153.

The 1920s

1. Fred E. Basten, *Max Factor*, p. 55.
2. Teresa Riordan, *Inventing Beauty*, p. 45.
3. *The Powder and the Glory*, DVD.
4. Recounted in Richard Corson, *Fashions in Makeup*, p. 500.
5. Kimberly-Clark, www.kleenex.com, "Kleenex Brand Product and Story."
6. Recounted in Richard Corson, *Fashions in Makeup*, p. 481.
7. Daniel Delis Hill, *Advertising to the American Woman*, p. 93.
8. Richard Corson, *Fashions in Makeup*, p. 484.
9. *The Powder and the Glory,* DVD.
10. The George W. Luft Co., *Tangee: The Art of Make-up*, p. 6.
11. The George W. Luft Co., *Tangee: The Art of Make-up*, p. 10.
12. Fred E. Basten, Robert Salvatore, and Paul A. Kaufman. *Max Factor's Hollywood*, p. 90.
13. Recounted in Richard Corson, *Fashions in Makeup*, p. 476.
14. James Bennett, Cosmeticsandskin.com, "Maybelline".
15. Recounted in Richard Corson, *Fashions in Makeup*, p, 462.
16. Richard Corson, *Fashions in Makeup*, p. 469.
17. Teresa Riordan, *Inventing Beauty*, p. 45-46.
18. Richard Corson, *Fashions in Makeup*, p. 481.
19. Fred E. Basten, Robert Salvatore, and Paul A. Kaufman. *Max Factor's Hollywood*, p. 76.
20. Richard Corson, *Fashions in Makeup*, p. 479.
21. James Bennett, cosmeticsandskin.com, "A Glowing Complexion."
22. James Bennett, cosmeticsandskin.com, "1920 Cosmetic Timeline."
23. Richard Corson, *Fashions in Makeup*, p. 456.
24. Lois W. Banner, *American Beauty*, p. 277.
25. Richard Corson, *Fashions in Makeup*, p. 484.
26. Kathy Peiss, *Hope in a Jar*, p. 150.
27. James Bennett, cosmeticsandskin.com, "1920 Cosmetic Timeline."
28. Helena Rubenstein, *This Way to Beauty*, p. 80.

29. Helena Rubenstein, *This Way to Beauty*, p. 88.
30. Richard Corson, *Fashions in Makeup*, p. 462.
31. Perc Westmore, et al. *Westmore Beauty Book*, p. 214.

The 1930s
1. *The Powder and the Glory*, DVD.
2. Kathy Peiss, *Hope in a Jar*, p. 124.
2. Virginia Vincent, *Make-up*, p. 1.
3. Fred E. Basten, *Max Factor*, p. 117.
4. Richard Corson, *Fashions in Makeup*, p 516.
5. Virginia Vincent, *Make-up*, p. 10.
6. Teresa Riordan, *Inventing Beauty*, p. 3.
7. James Bennett, cosmeticsandskin.com.
8. James Bennett, cosmeticsandskin.com. "Rachel."
9. Richard Corson, *Fashions in Makeup*, p. 500.
10. Richard Corson, *Fashions in Makeup*, p 498.
11. Jane Gordon, *Technique for Beauty*, p. 152.
12. Richard Corson, *Fashions in Makeup*, p. 496.
13. Richard Corson, *Fashions in Makeup*, p. 516.
14. Virginia Vincent, *Make-up*, p. 16.
15. Virginia Vincent, *Make-up*, p. 22.
16. Virginia Vincent, *Make-up*, p. 6.
17. Helena Rubenstein, *This Way to Beauty*, p. 89.
18. Fred E. Basten, *Max Factor*, p. 160.
19. James Bennett, Cosmeticsandskin.com. "Max and the Tube".
20. *Mechanix Illustrated*, September 1939, p. 71.

The 1940s
1. Kathy Peiss, *Hope in a Jar*, p. 245.
2. Recounted in Fred E. Basten, Robert Salvatore, and Paul A. Kaufman. *Max Factor's Hollywood*, p. 164.
3. Richard Corson, *Fashions in Makeup*, p. 530.
4. Angela Bjork and Daniel Turudich, *Vintage Face*, p. 41.
5. Jane Gordon, *Technique for Beauty*, p. 154.
6. Jane Gordon, *Technique for Beauty*, p. 153.
7. Jane Gordon, *Technique for Beauty*, p. 152.
8. Jane Gordon, *Technique for Beauty*, p. 531.
9. Jane Gordon, *Technique for Beauty*, p. 112.
10. Angela Bjork and Daniel Turudich, *Vintage Face*, p. 40.
11. Teresa Riordan, *Inventing Beauty*, p. 151.
12. Jane Gordon, *Technique for Beauty*, p. 152.
13. Richard Corson, *Fashions in Makeup*, p. 530.
14. Jane Gordon, *Technique for Beauty*, p. 154.
15. Jane Gordon, *Technique for Beauty*, p. 154.
16. Richard Corson, *Fashions in Makeup*, p. 333.
17. Richard Corson, *Fashions in Makeup*, p. 519.
18. Kathy Peiss, *Hope in a Jar*, p. 240.
19. Kathy Peiss, *Hope in a Jar*, p. 240.
20. Jane Gordon, *Technique for Beauty*, p. 453.
21. Jane Gordon, *Technique for Beauty*, p. 312.
22. Jane Gordon, *Technique for Beauty*, p. 314.
23. Mike Brown. *The 1940s Look*, p. 112.
24. Andrew P. Tobias, *Fire and Ice*, p. 81.
25. Mike Brown. *The 1940s Look*, p. 110, 116.
26. Mike Brown. *The 1940s Look*, p. 112.
27. Carl Zebrowski, www.americainwwii.com, "A Product with Legs."
28. Mike Brown. *The 1940s Look*, p. 114.
29. Jane Gordon, *Technique for Beauty*, p. 456.
30. Dave Lackie. *Cosmetic Magazine*, March 10, 2010.
31. Jane Gordon, *Technique for Beauty*, p. 455, 457.
32. Jane Gordon, *Technique for Beauty*, p. 457.
33. Jane Gordon, *Technique for Beauty*, p. 452.
34. Fred E. Basten, *Max Factor*, p. 174.
35. Richard Corson, *Fashions in Makeup*, p. 453.

The 1950s

1. Richard Corson, *Fashions in Makeup,* p. 546.
2. Richard Corson, *Fashions in Makeup,* p. 459.
3. Teresa Riordan, *Inventing Beauty,* p. 10.
4. Recounted in Richard Corson, *Fashions in Makeup,* p. 534.
5. Richard Corson, *Fashions in Makeup,* p. 535.
6. Richard Corson, *Fashions in Makeup,* p. 533.
7. Richard Corson, *Fashions in Makeup,* p. 539.
8. Richard Corson, *Fashions in Makeup,* p. 545.
9. Richard Corson, *Fashions in Makeup,* p. 539.
10. James Bennett, cosmeticsandskin.com, "1930 Cosmetic Timeline."
11. Kathy Peiss, *Hope in a Jar,* p. 246.
12. Andrew P. Tobias, *Fire and Ice,* p. 117.
13. *The Powder and the Glory,* DVD.

The 1960s

1. Richard Corson, *Fashions in Makeup,* p. 550.
2. Richard Corson, *Fashions in Makeup,* p. 561.
3. Richard Corson, *Fashions in Makeup,* p. 556.
4. Richard Corson, *Fashions in Makeup,* p. 556.
5. Richard Corson, *Fashions in Makeup,* p. 550.
6. Kathy Peiss, *Hope in a Jar,* p. 247.
7. *The Powder and the Glory,* DVD.
8. Richard Corson, *Fashions in Makeup,* p. 552.
9. Richard Corson, *Fashions in Makeup,* p. 560.
10. Richard Corson, *Fashions in Makeup,* p. 560.
11. Richard Corson, *Fashions in Makeup,* p. 553.

Bibliography

Alpert, Arlene, et al. *Milady's Standard: Cosmetology*. New York: Thomson Learning, 2004.

Baird, John F. *Make-up: A Manual for the Use of Actors, Amateur and Professional*. New York: Samuel French, 1941.

Banner, Lois W. *American Beauty*. New York: Knopf, 1983.

Basten, Fred E. *Max Factor: The Man Who Changed the Face of the World*. New York: Arcade Publishing, 2008.

Basten, Fred E., Robert Salvatore, and Paul A. Kaufman. *Max Factor's Hollywood: Glamour, Movies, Make-up*. Los Angeles: General Publishing Group, 1995.

Bjork, Angela and Daniel Turudich. *Vintage Face: Period Looks From the 1920s, 1930s, 1940s, & 1950s*. Long Beach, California: Streamline Press, 2001.

Bonomo, Joe. *Make-up and Live!*. Brooklyn: Joe Bonomo, 1938.

Brown, Mike. *The 1940s Look: Recreating the Fashions, Hairstyles and Make-up of the Second World War*. Sevenoaks, United Kingdon: Sabrestorm, 2007.

Corson, Richard. *Fashions in Makeup: From Ancient to Modern Times*. London: Peter Owen, 1972.

Factor, Max. *The New Art of Society Make-up*. Hollywood: Max Factor Studios, 1928.

Garrett, Murray. *Hollywood Candid: A Photographer Remembers*. New York: Harry N. Abrams, 2000.

Gordon, Jane. *Technique for Beauty*. London: Faber and Faber, 1940.

Hill, Daniel Delis. *Advertising to the American Woman*. Ohio: Ohio State University Press, 2002.

Hurrell, George. *50 Years of Photographing Hollywood: The Hurrell Style*. New York: Greenwich House, 1983.

Kobal, John. *The Art of the Great Hollywood Portrait Photographers, 1925-1940*. New York: Harrison House, 1987.

Lackie, Dave. "Elizabeth Arden: Canada's Beauty Queen." *Cosmetic Magazine*, March 10, 2010.

Lobenthal, Joel. *Radical Rags: Fashions of the Sixties*. New York: Abbeville Press, 1990.

Manual on Theory and Practice of Beauty Culture. USA: Milady, 1939.

Mechanix Illustrated. Louisville, Kentucky: Fawcett Publications, Inc., September 1939.

Peiss, Kathy. *Hope In A Jar: The Making of America's Beauty Culture*. New York: Henry Holt and Company, 1998.

Pendergrast, Mark. *Mirror Mirror: A History of the Human Love Affair with Reflection*. New York: Basic Books, 2003.

Riordan, Teresa. *Inventing Beauty: A History of the Innovations That Have Made Us Beautiful*. New York: Broadway Books, 2004.

Riva, Maria. *Marlene Dietrich*. New York: Ballantine Books, 1992.

Rubenstein, Helena. *This Way to Beauty*. London: George G. Harrap and Co. LTD, 1937.

Sherrow, Victoria. *Encyclopedia of Hair: A Cultural History*. Westport: Greenwood Press, 2006.

The George W. Luft Co. *Tangee: The Art of Make-up*. New York: The George W. Luft Co., 1930.

Tobias, Andrew P. *Fire and Ice: The Story of Charles Revson – The Man Who Built the Revlon Empire*. New York: William Morrow and Company, Inc., 1976.

Vieira, Mark A. *Hurrell's Hollywood Portraits: The Chapman Collection*. New York: Harry N. Abrams, 1997.

Vincent, Virginia. *Make-up*. USA: Bramcost Publications, 1932.

Vogue. New York: Conde Nast, November 1946.

Vogue. New York: Conde Nast, April 1963.

Vogue. New York: Conde Nast, October 1966.

Vogue's Beauty Book. New York: Conde Nast, 1957.

Weingarten, Rachel C. *Hello Gorgeous! Beauty Products in America '40s-'60s*. Portland, Oregon: Collectors Press, 2006.

Westmore, Perc, et al. *Westmore Beauty Book*. USA: Bramcost Publications, 1956.

Zimmerman, Tom. *Light and Illusion: The Hollywood Portraits of Ray Jones*. Glendale, California: Balcony Press, 1998.

DVDs

Hollywood Biographies: The Leading Ladies. DVD. Passport Video. 2006. 5-Disc Series.

The Powder and the Glory. DVD. PBS Home Video. 2008.

Websites

Bennett, James. "Cosmetics and Skin." www.cosmeticsandskin.com

"Maybelline New York: Our History." www.maybelline.co.uk/ABOUT_US/Our_History.aspx

"The Cleo Craze." taylortribute.com/Elizabeth Taylor - Cleopatra Craze-01.html

"Kleenex® Brand Product and Story." www.kleenex.com/BrandStory.aspx

"Jean Patou." www.fragrantica.com/news/Jean-Patou-439.html

"Wikipedia." www.wikipedia.com

Zebrowski, Carl, "A Product with Legs", www.americainwwii.com/stories/productwithlegs

Image Credits

P. 1 courtesy of The Kobal Collection, P. 8 Library of Congress, Prints and Photographs Division, [reproduction number LC-DIG-csas-06160], P.10 Library of Congress, Prints and Photographs Division, [reproduction number LC-DIG-ggbain-31568], Women of Protest: Photographs from the Records of the National Woman's Party, Manuscript Division, Library of Congress, Washington, D.C., P. 11 courtesy of The Kobal Collection, P. 35 courtesy of Wikimedia, P. 53 Mechanix Illustrated, September 1939, P. 60 Library of Congress, Prints and Photographs Division, [reproduction number LC-DIG-fsac-1a35287], P. 61 Library of Congress, Prints and Photographs Division, [reproduction number LC-DIG-fsac-1a34899], Library of Congress, Prints and Photographs Division, [reproduction number LC-DIG-fsa-8e09024], P. 63 courtesy Elizabeth Arden, Inc., P. 64 courtesy Richards and Appleby Ltd., P. 65 courtesy Elizabeth Arden, Inc.

About the author

Hair and makeup artist Lauren Rennells works in the photography and film industry. She freelances providing unique designs for advertisements, films, television and private clients. Her passion for beauty of the past led her to write *Retro Makeup: Techniques for Applying the Vintage Look* and *Vintage Hairstyling: Retro Styles with Step-by-Step Techniques*. She also provides more information and techniques for historical hair and makeup on her blog at www.bobbypinblog.blogspot.com.

Titles from HRST Books:

Vintage Hairstyling:
Retro Styles with Step-by-Step Techniques
MSRP $36.95 US

Retro Makeup:
Techniques for Applying the Vintage Look
MSRP $23.95 US

To order other books, go to www.hrstbooks.com for credit card orders or to find a retailer near you.

Mail order with check or money order, please include shipping of $5.00 US per book or $13.00 US per book for shipping outside the United States. Colorado residents, please include 7.72% sales tax.

Please send payment to:
HRST Books
P.O. Box 18429
Denver, Colorado
80218

For more information either email info@hrstbooks.com or call (303) 832-7260.